CONTENTS

Grade

CHAPTER 1 • Data, Statistics, and Graphs

CHAPTER 2 • Add and Subtract Whole Numbers and Decimals

Chapter 3 • Multiply Whole Numbers and Decimals

Chapter 4 • Dividing Whole Numbers and Decimals

Chapter 5 • Number Theory and Fraction Concepts

Chapter 6 • Add and Subtract Fractions and Mixed Numbers

Chapter 7 • Multiplying and Dividing Fractions and Mixed Numbers

CHAPTER 8 • Geometry

CHAPTER 9 • Introduction to Algebra

CHAPTER 10 • Ratios and Proportions

CHAPTER 11 • Percent

CHAPTER 12 • Probability

CHAPTER 13 • Perimeter, Area, and Volume

CHAPTER 14 • Integers

Practice 1

Name: ____________________

Collect, Organize, and Display Data

Use the frequency table and pictograph for problems 1–4.

HOURS SPENT SLEEPING LAST NIGHT

Hours	Tally	Frequency
5		0
6	II	2
7	~~IIII~~ ~~IIII~~	10
8	~~IIII~~ ~~IIII~~ IIII	14
9	III	3
10	I	1
11		0

Hours Spent Sleeping Last Night

5	
6	●
7	● ● ● ● ●
8	● ● ● ● ● ● ●
9	● ◖
10	◖
11	

Key: ● = 2 students

1. Which number of hours did the most students say they spent sleeping last night?

____

2. How many students spent 7 or 8 hours sleeping last night?

____

3. How would the pictograph change if no students slept for more than 9 hours?

____

4. Why are frequency tables useful for collecting data?

____

Use the line plot for problem 5.

5. Identify any clusters or gaps in the data. What conclusions can you make?

____

Number of Pairs of Sneakers My Classmates Own

0	1	2	3	4	5
x	x x x x x	x x x x x x x x x		x	

Name: ____________________

BAR GRAPHS

Use the bar graph for problems 1–3.

1. Which river is longest? About how long is it?

2. About how much longer is the Colorado River than the St. Lawrence River?

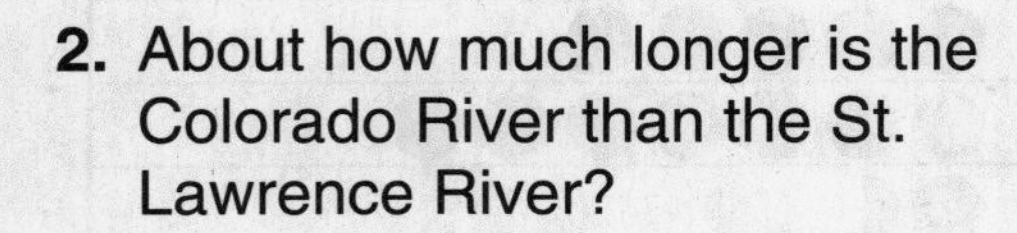

3. If the scale were changed to a smaller interval, how would this graph be different?

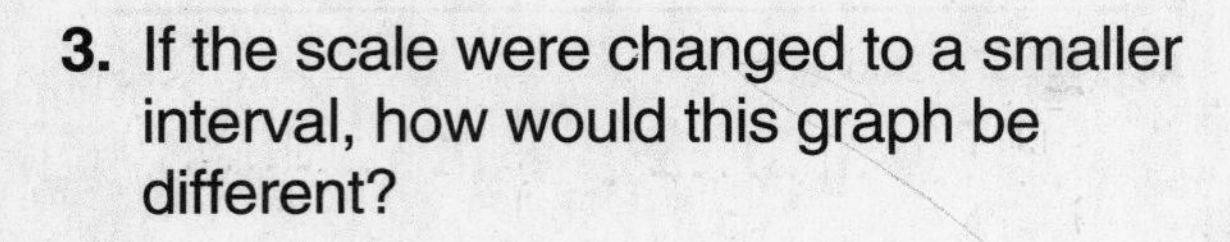

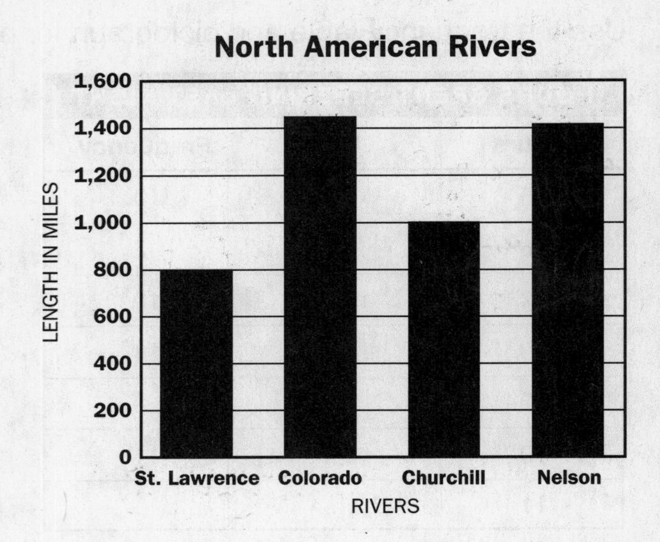

On a separate sheet of paper, make a bar graph for the data in each table below.

4.

WORLD RIVERS	
River	**Length in Miles**
Uruguay	1,000
Brahmaputra	1,800
Euphrates	2,235
Gambia	700
Salween	1,500

5.

CAR SALES		
Month	**4-door**	**2-door**
Jan.	7	9
Feb.	5	8
Mar.	8	10
April	9	11
May	12	13

Use the graph for problems 6–7.

6. Where were the greatest number of fifth and sixth graders born?

7. In which two countries were the same number of fifth graders born?

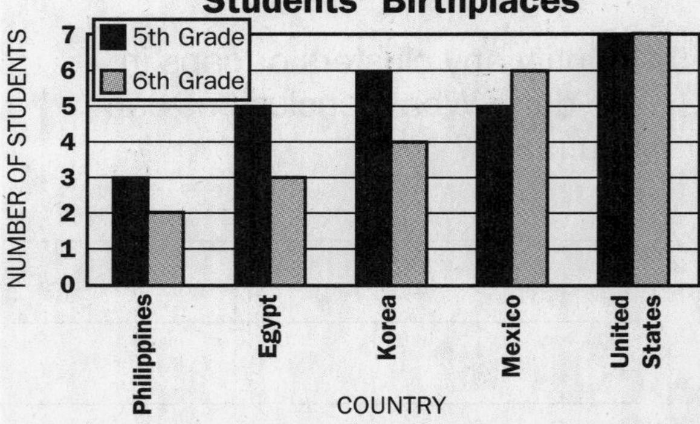

Name: ______________________________

Problem-Solving Strategy: Make a Table

✔ Read
✔ Plan
✔ Solve
✔ Look Back

Solve using the make-a-table strategy.

1. The data shows the results of a survey of the favorite lunches of sixth graders. Make a table to display the data.

SURVEY RESULTS		
tuna fish	ravioli	grilled cheese
pizza	ravioli	pizza
pizza	pizza	grilled cheese
grilled cheese	grilled cheese	pizza
tuna fish	pizza	ravioli
ravioli	ravioli	pizza

2. Which lunch is the favorite among sixth graders?

____

3. Which lunch is the least favorite among sixth graders?

____

4. Do more students say their favorite lunch is grilled cheese or ravioli?

____

Solve using any method.

5. A movie theater complex shows movies in 5 different theaters. On Monday night, 13 people see the movie in Theater A, 17 see the one in Theater B, 16 see the one in Theater C, 14 see the one in Theater D, and 19 people see the one in Theater E. Which theater represents the median number of people attending each theater?

____

6. Theater A seats 75 people, Theater B seats 100 people, Theater C seats 100 people, Theater D seats 75 people, and Theater E seats 100 people. What is the mean for the number of seats in the five theaters?

____

____

7. On Saturday night, 85 people see the movie in Theater E. If tickets cost \$6.75, about how much does the theater complex take in for that movie?

____

____

8. On Wednesday, 2 tickets are sold for the price of one. Twenty-four people see the movie in Theater A, 28 see the one in Theater B, 31 see the one in Theater C, 42 see the one in Theater D, and 47 see the one in Theater E. If tickets cost \$6.75, about how much does the theater complex take in that night?

____

Name: ______________________

LINE GRAPHS

Use the double-line graph for problems 1–4.

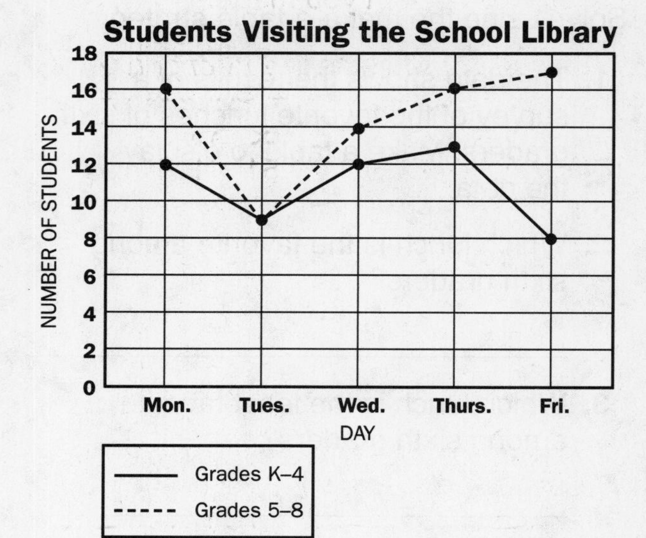

1. How many more students in grades 5–8 visited the library on Monday than students in grades K–4?

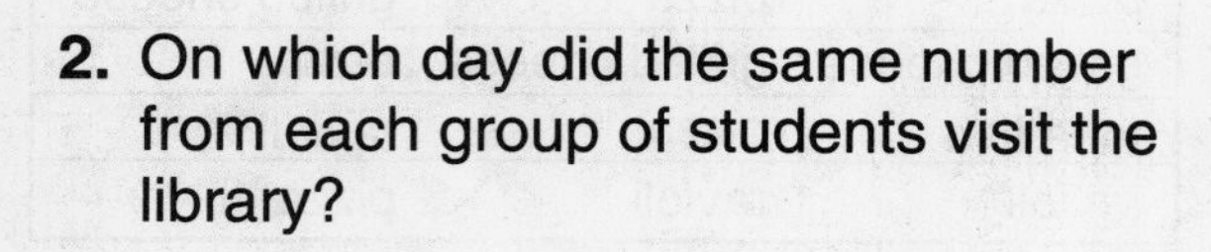

2. On which day did the same number from each group of students visit the library?

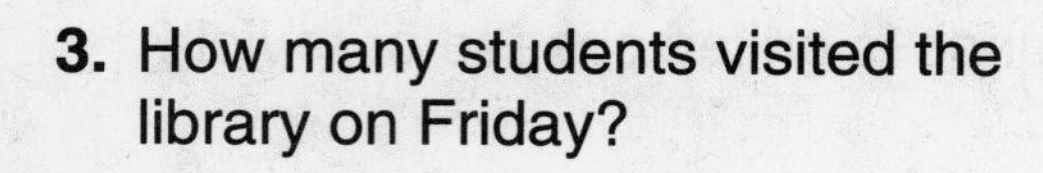

3. How many students visited the library on Friday?

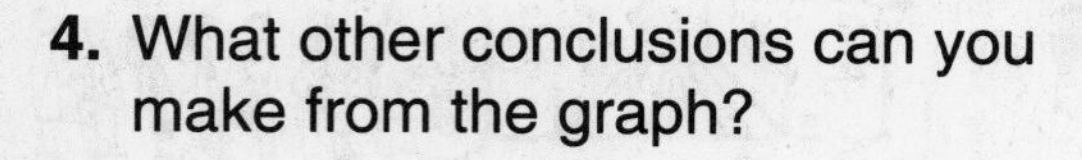

4. What other conclusions can you make from the graph?

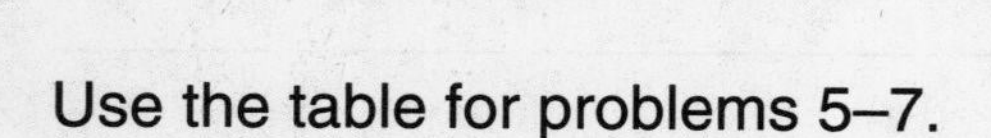

Use the table for problems 5–7.

DAILY HIGH TEMPERATURES (°F)		
Day	**High**	**Low**
Monday	55°	32°
Tuesday	52°	29°
Wednesday	57°	33°
Thursday	45°	27°
Friday	47°	28°
Saturday	50°	30°
Sunday	52°	31°

5. Make a double-line graph for the data in the table.

6. On which day of the week was the highest temperature recorded? the lowest temperature?

7. Between which two days was there the greatest difference in their high temperatures? On which day did the temperature vary the most?

Name: ______________________________

Stem-and-Leaf Plots

Make a stem-and-leaf plot for each set of data. Draw conclusions based on the plot you made.

1. Number of coins in student banks:

60	68	43	20	65	38	34	67
32	62	20	45	51	21	60	29

Conclusions: ______________________________

2. Number of books on library shelves:

25	17	19	10	13	11	16	15
25	10	10	11	10	23	15	

Conclusions: ______________________________

3. Number of steps taken while walking for 30 seconds:

38	63	45	68	74	50
71	69	70	63	72	57
78	65	67	68	52	44

Conclusions: ______________________________

4. Quiz scores of students in Mrs. Baker's class:

76	92	79	71	86	87	77	89
83	80	93	87	76	72	77	87
75	92	86	88	82	84	87	74
85	82	93					

Conclusions: ______________________________

Use the stem-and-leaf plot for problems 5–7.

Minutes Spent Riding the Bus

Stem	Leaf
1	1 4 4 5 8
2	4 4 5 7
3	1 1 2 2 2 3 5 7 7
4	2 4 5

Key: 1 | 1 = 11

5. How many students are represented by the plot?

____

6. What is the range, median, and mode of the data?

____

7. How many students ride the bus for more than 15 minutes?

____

Name: ______________________________

SAMPLING AND PREDICTING

Identify the population and sample in each situation.
Tell if you think the sample is representative.

1. Survey half the members of the football squad to find out if the squad wants to practice on Monday or on Tuesday.

2. In a class of 19 students, ask 7 students if they enjoy playing sports.

3. In a school of 150 students, randomly choose the names of 3 students. Ask those students whom they would vote for in a school election.

4. Survey members of the faculty to find out if students believe the school day is too short.

5. Ask 3 of the 4 volunteer librarians if they enjoy working in the school library.

6. In a class of 18 sixth graders, ask the students who have won a sports award to name the favorite sport of the class.

7. In a class of 42 students, choose 25 students at random and ask them to count the number of sisters and brothers they have.

8. Ask your best friend to name the favorite food of parents.

9. Ask three teachers if they believe there are enough parking spaces in the school lot.

10. Ask all 31 students in a class what their favorite day of the week is.

Practice 9

Name: ______________________________

Problem Solving: Choose the Appropriate Graph

✔ Read
✔ Plan
✔ Solve
✔ Look Back

Solve.

SPEEDS OF ANIMALS	
Animal	**Speed (mph)**
cheetah	70
wildebeest	50
elk	45
coyote	43
rabbit	35
reindeer	32
warthog	30
elephant	25

AVERAGE LIFE SPAN OF ANIMALS	
Animal	**Life Span (years)**
African elephant	35
grizzly bear	25
baboon	20
cow	15
sheep	12
squirrel	10
kangaroo	7
mouse	3

BIRDS SPOTTED AT BIRD FEEDER IN FALL/WINTER	
Month	**Number of Birds**
October	10
November	15
December	23
January	39
February	47

1. What type of graph would you use to display the data for the speeds of animals? Why?

____

____

2. What type of graph would you use to display the data for the average life span of animals? Why?

____

____

3. What type of graph would you use to display the data for birds spotted at a bird feeder in fall/winter? Why?

____

____

Solve using any method.

4. Dave works four days a week. On Wednesdays he earns $24, Thursdays $26, Saturdays $30, and Sundays $35. How much more does he make on weekends?

____

5. Annie works 4 hours on Wednesday, 4 hours on Thursday, 5 hours on Saturday, and 6 hours on Sunday. What is her average number of hours?

____

6. Jack makes $24.75 in one day. If he works about 5 hours each day, about how much does he earn per hour?

____

Name: ______________________________

EXPONENTS

Write using an exponent.

1. $4 \times 4 \times 4$ ________
2. $2 \times 2 \times 2 \times 2 \times 2 \times 2$ ________
3. $9 \times 9 \times 9 \times 9$ ________
4. $1 \times 1 \times 1 \times 1 \times 1$ ________
5. $5 \times 5 \times 5 \times 5$ ________
6. $3 \times 3 \times 3 \times 3 \times 3 \times 3 \times 3$ ________
7. 6×6 ________
8. $350 \times 350 \times 350$ ________
9. $10 \times 10 \times 10 \times 10$ ________

Write in standard form.

10. 1^3 ________
11. 100^3 ________
12. 10^4 ________
13. 7^3 ________
14. 25^2 ________
15. 3^5 ________
16. 5^4 ________
17. 24^2 ________
18. 8^3 ________
19. 18^2 ________
20. 4^4 ________
21. 2^7 ________
22. 26^2 ________
23. 6^3 ________
24. 12^3 ________
25. 6^4 ________

Complete the tables.

26.

Exponent Form	Factor Form	Standard Form
10^2		100
10^5	$10 \times 10 \times 10 \times 10 \times 10$	
	$10 \times 10 \times 10$	1,000

27.

Exponent Form	Factor Form	Standard Form
8^3	$8 \times 8 \times 8$	
8^4		4,096
	8×8	64

Name: ______________________

Whole Numbers

Name the place and the value of the digit 4 in each number.

1. 41,053 ______________

2. 634,950 ______________

3. 2,322,649 ______________

4. 190,489 ______________

5. 84,913 ______________

6. 43,980,572,316 ______________

7. 78,364 ______________

8. 24,711,685 ______________

9. 467,508 ______________

10. 457,892,731 ______________

Write the number in standard form.

11. 4 thousand, 3 hundred ______________

12. 52 thousand, 15 ______________

13. 60 million, 25 thousand ______________

14. 8 billion, 90 million ______________

15. $(4 \times 10^4) + (3 \times 10^2) + (3 \times 10^1) + 4$ ______________

16. 6 billion, 15 ______________

17. 19 million, 160 thousand ______________

18. $(7 \times 10^5) + (3 \times 10^2) + 6$ ______________

Use the table for problems 19–20.

19. Write the expanded form and word name for the distance between Mercury and the sun.

____

____

20. The distance between Mars and the sun is 141,710,000 miles. What is the place and the value of the digit 4 in the number 141,710,000?

____

AVERAGE DISTANCE FROM THE SUN IN MILES	
Planet	**Distance**
Mercury	36,000,000
Earth	92,900,000
Mars	141,710,000
Saturn	887,000,000
Pluto	3,674,000,000

Name: ______________________________

DECIMALS

Name the place and the value of the digit 6 in each number.

1. 0.065 ______________________

2. 0.69 ______________________

3. 68.92 ______________________

4. 0.243691 ______________________

5. 741.0063 ______________________

6. 0.48976 ______________________

7. 34.961 ______________________

8. 9.87602 ______________________

Complete the chart.

	Decimal	Fraction or Mixed Number
9.	0.3	
10.		$\frac{46}{100}$
11.		$8\frac{2}{10}$
12.	7.36	
13.		$27\frac{789}{1,000}$
14.	6.9025	
15.		$\frac{1,086}{10,000}$
16.		$3\frac{507}{1,000}$

Write the number in standard form.

17. The length of a year on the planet Mercury is eighty-seven and ninety-seven hundredths Earth days.

____

18. The length of a year on the planet Venus is two hundred twenty-four and seven tenths Earth days.

____

Name: ______

Compare and Order Decimals

Write >, <, or =.

1. 2.6 ◯ 2.1
2. 3.060 ◯ 3.06
3. 14.3 ◯ 14.95
4. 5.63 ◯ 0.944
5. 92.8 ◯ 99.3
6. 73.04 ◯ 73.40
7. 145.6 ◯ 145.600
8. 118.5 ◯ 115.8
9. 0.017 ◯ 0.0170
10. 1.605 ◯ 1.56
11. 0.08 ◯ 0.6
12. $2 ◯ $2.00

Order the numbers from greatest to least.

13. 5.6, 6.1, 3.7 ______
14. 0.03, 14.6, 5.707 ______
15. $26, $26.11, $21.61 ______
16. 18.06, 18.60, 18.606 ______
17. 0.4390, 0.4389, 0.4392, 0.4399 ______
18. 0.7431, 0.4371, 0.7341, 0.4317 ______
19. 16.893, 16.894, 16.884, 16.983 ______
20. 34.0936, 33.0936, 33.0966, 33.0938 ______

Use the chart to solve problems 21, 22, and 23.

21. Which item costs the most?

______

22. Which item costs the least?

______

23. Order the prices from greatest to least.

______

GROCERY ITEMS	
box of cereal	$2.38
salad dressing	$2.23
bag of potatoes	$3.83
3 lb of rice	$3.22

Name: ______

MENTAL MATH: ESTIMATE SUMS AND DIFFERENCES

Estimate the sum or difference by rounding.

1. 23.4 − 12.96 ______ **2.** 8.07 − 5.963 ______ **3.** 487.664 + 217.02 ______

4. 727.92 − 230.1 ______ **5.** 51.3 + 19.093 ______ **6.** 502.6 − 390.05 ______

7. 12.298 + 57.073 ______ **8.** 7.42 + 2.7 ______ **9.** $76.82 + $23.09 ______

10. 5.035 − 2.19 ______ **11.** 48.625 + 61.7 ______ **12.** 874.57 − 267.3 ______

13. 84.3 − 32.858 ______ **14.** 6.005 + 390.05 ______ **15.** 246.75 − 41.9 ______

16. 4.83 + 9.489

17. 16.3 + 24.9

18. 79.86 − 43.92

19. 8.679 − 4.976

20. 23.9 + 79.99 + 6.433

21. $47.50 − 29.63

22. 8.79 + 14.321 + 6.030

23. 19.30 + 86.423 + 9.855

Use the chart to solve problems 24–25.

24. About how much would the largemouth bass, atlantic salmon, white perch, and rainbow trout weigh altogether?

______

25. Estimate the difference between the chinook salmon and the arctic char.

______

LARGEST FRESHWATER FISH CAUGHT BY LINE (pounds)	
Largemouth bass	22.25
White perch	4.75
Atlantic salmon	79.125
Mountain whitefish	5.375
Chinook salmon	97.25
Arctic char	32.5625
Florida gar	21.1875
Rainbow trout	42.125

Practice 15

Name: ______

ADD DECIMALS

Add. Remember to estimate.

1. $0.9 + 1.2$
2. $1.87 + 0.09$
3. $\$60.70 + 39.95$
4. $2.193 + 9.912$
5. $467.29 + 840.03$
6. $5.720 + 4.485$
7. $864 + 38.6$
8. $33.8 + 75$
9. $39.015 + 42.067$
10. $9.86 + 0.201$
11. $2.43 + 7.62$
12. $\$6.80 + 188.50$
13. $\$4.15 + 2.69 + 7.03$
14. $29.04 + 14.63 + 7.25$
15. $417.05 + 85.2 + 9.36$

16. 9.15 + 78.7 + 96.5 ______

17. 0.53 + 9.1 + 0.008 ______

18. 1.05 + 0.24 + 1.9 ______

19. 56.8 + 0.23 + 1.74 ______

20. \$62.10 + \$60 + \$19.50 ______

21. 706 + 82.2 + 7.67 ______

Algebra Complete the pattern. Write the rule for each pattern.

22. (3.2, 3), (3.5, 3), (3.8, 3), (____, 3), (4.4, 3)

______

23. (5, 1.6), (5, 1.8), (5, 2.0), (5, ____), (5, ____)

______

Solve.

24. Matthew put an empty dish on a scale. Its mass is 11.36 g. He then put a chemical, with a mass of 0.274 g, on the dish. What is the mass of the dish now?

______

25. Matthew puts three coins on the scale: a dime whose mass is 2.5 g, a penny whose mass is 3.25 g, and a quarter whose mass is 6.5 g. What is the total mass of the coins?

______

Name: ______

Subtract Decimals

Subtract. Remember to estimate.

1. 6.38 − 1.44
2. 7.13 − 3.97
3. \$9.01 − 8.90
4. 2.795 − 1.12
5. 8.302 − 1.395
6. 82.02 − 43.6
7. 826.8 − 731.8
8. 210 − 9.9
9. 30.521 − 0.376
10. 427 − 138.06
11. 63.7 − 4.68
12. 24.05 − 4.89
13. 70.19 − 1.78
14. 34 − 5.54
15. 62.504 − 53.7

16. \$8.10 − \$4.94 ______
17. 7.44 − 2.58 ______
18. 5.856 − 1.693 ______
19. 7.56 − 0.99 ______
20. 15.2 − 5.39 ______
21. 673 − 58.1 ______
22. 64.2 − 0.732 ______
23. 67 − 9.06 ______
24. 712 − 0.346 ______

Algebra Find the output.

25. **Rule:** Subtract 0.235.

Input	Output
2.03	______
36	______
6.851	______

26. **Rule:** Subtract 0.077.

Input	Output
0.7	______
0.77	______
0.7777	______

27. **Rule:** Subtract 12.47.

Input	Output
30	______
130	______
1,500	______

Solve.

28. Tyrone walks to the clothing store, which is 3.8 kilometers from his house. On the way he stops at the library, which is 0.9 kilometers from the store. How far does he walk?

______

29. At the clothing store, Tyrone buys a sweater for \$18.79. He gives the clerk \$20. How much change does he get?

______

Name: ____________________

Practice 17

Problem-Solving Strategy: Guess, Test, and Revise

✔ Read
✔ Plan
✔ Solve
✔ Look Back

Solve using the guess, test, and revise strategy.

1. Carlos wants to use the entire length of a 120-foot roll of wire fencing to make a rectangular outdoor enclosure for his new puppy. What will the length and width of the enclosure be if Carlos wants the width to be 20 feet less than the length?

   ____

2. What will the length and width of the enclosure be if Carlos decides to use only 100 feet of the roll of wire fencing and the width is 10 feet less than the length?

   ____

   ____

3. If Carlos used the entire length of a 152-foot roll of wire fencing, what would the length and width of a square enclosure be?

   ____

   ____

4. Inside the enclosure, Carlos wants to build a rectangular box for the puppy to sleep in. The length is 3 feet longer than the width and the perimeter of the box is 22 feet. What are the dimensions?

   ____

Solve using any method.

5. Carlos buys puppy treats. He has 4 fewer plastic bones than dog biscuits. He has 2 more dog biscuits than chew toys. If he has a total of 12 treats, how many does he have of each?

   ____

   ____

6. Carlos used coins to buy the treats. Altogether he had $3.30. If he had 9 more nickels than dimes and 12 fewer quarters than nickels, how many of each did he have?

   ____

   ____

7. **Spatial Reasoning** What symbol occurs next in the sequence?

   <<=>=<<=>=<<=> ________

8. Write a series of five decimal numbers that increase by 0.2 and add up to a total of 5.

   ____

Name: ______________________

Practice 18

ADDITION AND SUBTRACTION EXPRESSIONS

Evaluate each expression.

1. $56 + w$ for $w = 451$ ________
2. $u + 712$ for $u = 9$ ________
3. $a + 94$ for $a = 3.1$ ________
4. $m + 909$ for $m = 0.3$ ________
5. $8 + h$ for $h = 73.9$ ________
6. $c - 3.2$ for $c = 11.4$ ________
7. $j - 0.23$ for $j = 0.6$ ________
8. $z - 5.7$ for $z = 18$ ________
9. $206 - p$ for $p = 77.1$ ________
10. $8.1 - b$ for $b = 0.76$ ________
11. $461 - s$ for $s = 239.8$ ________
12. $174 + n$ for $n = 2.15$ ________

Write an expression for the situation.

13. Your weight if you weighed $129\frac{3}{4}$ pounds and you lost m pounds

____

14. Your weight if you weighed $134\frac{1}{2}$ pounds and gained p pounds

____

15. The total cost c of a department store purchase, not including a sales tax of $1.42

____

16. The weight of a crate of apples if the apples weigh 20 pounds and the weight of the crate is not known

____

Solve.

17. Alani's math quiz score was x points short of 100. Write an expression for Alani's score on the quiz.

____

18. Ellis estimates he studies 1.5 hours each night. Write an expression for the number of hours he would need to study if he wanted to study for an additional y number of hours each night.

____

Name: ____________________

Metric Units of Length

Tell whether you would use *km, m, cm,* or *mm* to measure.

1. height of a classroom desk ________

2. width of a garage ________

3. thickness of a comic book ________

4. distance to the moon ________

5. length of a soccer field ________

6. width of a lampshade ________

Estimate. Then use a metric ruler or tape measure to measure.

7. length of a paper clip ________

8. height of a bookshelf ________

9. thickness of an eraser ________

10. length of a chalkboard ________

11. thickness of a desktop ________

12. width of a sheet of paper ________

Ring the letter of the best estimate.

13. the height of your teacher's desk — **a.** 0.91 mm **b.** 0.91 cm **c.** 0.91 m

14. the width of a shoe — **a.** 9 cm **b.** 9 m **c.** 9 km

15. the length of a fork — **a.** 188 mm **b.** 188 cm **c.** 188 m

16. the distance from Chicago, IL, to Milwaukee, WI — **a.** 150 cm **b.** 150 m **c.** 150 km

17. thickness of a nickel — **a.** 2 mm **b.** 2 cm **c.** 2 m

18. length of a ruler — **a.** 30 mm **b.** 30 cm **c.** 3 km

19. distance from New York to Ohio — **a.** 1,000 cm **b.** 1,000 m **c.** 1,000 km

Solve.

20. Patty's town is 17,342 meters long. Her cousin Jack's town is 9,843 meters long. How much longer is Patty's town than Jack's, in meters?

____

21. To train for the event, Patty ran 2.350 km the first day, 4.680 km the second day, and 5.255 km the third day. How many kilometers did she run in these three days?

____

Name: ______________________________

Metric Units of Mass and Capacity

Name an appropriate unit of capacity or mass.

1. mass of an elephant ________
2. capacity of a bucket ________
3. mass of a cat ________
4. capacity of a vase ________
5. mass of a calculator ________
6. capacity of a teacup ________
7. mass of a dollar bill ________
8. capacity of a swimming pool ________
9. mass of a stapler ________
10. mass of an apple ________
11. capacity of a baby food jar ________
12. mass of a tractor ________
13. capacity of shampoo bottle ________

Write the letter of the best estimate.

14. A coffee cup holds about ______ of coffee. **a.** 2.5 mL **b.** 25 mL **c.** 250 mL
15. An apple has a mass of about ______. **a.** 175 mg **b.** 175 g **c.** 175 kg
16. The mass of a safety pin is about ______. **a.** 1 mg **b.** 1 g **c.** 1 kg
17. A small can of soup holds about ______. **a.** 6 mL **b.** 60 mL **c.** 600 mL
18. A car has a mass of about ______. **a.** 1,250 mg **b.** 1,250 g **c.** 1,250 kg
19. A baseball has a mass of about ______. **a.** 200 g **b.** 200 kg **c.** 200 mg
20. A watermelon has a mass of about ______. **a.** 10 g **b.** 10 T **c.** 10 kg

Solve.

21. Tanya has a 5-liter punch bowl. She bought 2 juice containers that hold 2.75 liters and 1.25 liters. If she buys one more container, how much punch can it hold?

    ____

22. Tanya bought bags of ice that weigh 6 kilograms, 4.5 kilograms, and 5.75 kilograms. What is the total weight of the ice?

    ____

Name: ______________________________

Practice 21

Problem Solving: Use Underestimates and Overestimates

✔ Read
✔ Plan
✔ Solve
✔ Look Back

Solve.

1. A local hardware store owner's expenses this week have been \$342.25, \$67.84, \$83.39, \$46.98, and \$373.49. About how much income must the store make to cover the expenses? Should she overestimate or underestimate her expenses?

____

____

____

____

2. Leah plans to use her allowance money to buy new wallpaper that sells for \$89.95. In the last 5 months she has saved \$12.55, \$15.75, \$18, \$16.80, and \$21.25. Should she overestimate or underestimate her savings? Did she save enough?

____

____

____

____

3. Patrice estimates that it will take her 12 hours to paint her home. Should she underestimate or overestimate the number of hours that she will need?

____

____

____

____

4. Patrice estimates she will need 9 gallons of paint. Should she underestimate or overestimate the number of gallons that will be needed?

____

____

____

Solve using any method.

5. The Milk River in Alberta, Canada, and Montana is 25^2 miles long. Write the length in standard form.

____

6. A super computer can perform 100 million calculations in one second. Write the number in standard form.

____

Name: ______________________________

MENTAL MATH: PATTERNS AND PROPERTIES

Complete the patterns.

1. $84 \times 1 = 84$

$84 \times 10 =$ ________

$84 \times 100 =$ ________

$84 \times 1{,}000 =$ ________

2. $2 \times 8 = 16$

$2 \times 80 =$ ________

$20 \times 80 =$ ________

$20 \times 800 =$ ________

3. $3 \times 5 = 15$

$3 \times 50 =$ ________

$3 \times 500 =$ ________

$3 \times 5{,}000 =$ ________

Algebra Find the missing number. Name the property of multiplication you used.

4. ____ $\times 14 = 14 \times 7$ ________________

5. $34 \times 6 \times$ ____ $= 0$ ________________

6. $5 \times$ ____ $= 5$ ________________

7. $5 \times ($____ $+ 3) = (5 \times 20) + (5 \times 3)$ ________________

8. $(18 \times 26) \times 30 =$ ____ $\times (26 \times 30)$ ________________

Multiply mentally.

9. 20×30 ________

10. 90×70 ________

11. 30×700 ________

12. $\$5 \times 75$ ________

13. $250 \times 2 \times 0$ ________

14. $\$13 \times 6$ ________

15. 32×9 ________

16. $2{,}000 \times \$8$ ________

17. 300×400 ________

18. $\$9{,}000 \times 30 =$ ________

19. $3 \times 12 \times 2 =$ ________

20. $900 \times 600 =$ ________

Solve.

21. A cornfield has 40 rows of corn with 72 stalks of corn in each row. How many stalks are there?

____

22. An orchard has 16 rows of apple trees. If there are 9 trees in each row, how many apple trees are there?

____

Name: ______________________________ **Practice 23**

Mental Math: Estimate Products

Estimate the product.

1. 3×203 ________
2. $9 \times \$6.35$ ________
3. 4.4×9.78 ________
4. $\$86.43 \times 39$ ________
5. 92×34 ________
6. 64.70×3.1 ________
7. 67×81.52 ________
8. 14×159.05 ________
9. 38.64×2.60 ________
10. 761×855 ________
11. $930 \times \$4.78$ ________
12. 78.90×54.012 ________
13. $\$3.04 \times 1{,}873$ ________
14. 6×683.672 ________
15. 12×162.94 ________
16. 18×492.64 ________
17. 3×302.299 ________
18. 62.24×929 ________

Estimate. Write > or <.

19. 81.3×64.1 ◯ 4,251
20. 7×84.1 ◯ 516
21. 4.9×525 ◯ 2,750
22. 5.21×1.793 ◯ 12.6
23. $25 \times \$9.82$ ◯ \$362
24. 82.7×64.3 ◯ 50,213
25. 40.2×53.2 ◯ 1,876.8
26. 78×665 ◯ 559,010
27. 36×928 ◯ 31,426
28. 62.46×123.4 ◯ 7,939
29. $\$85.62 \times 425$ ◯ \$34,165
30. 98.25×428 ◯ 4,269
31. 5.92×258 ◯ 1,294
32. $\$168 \times 22.75$ ◯ \$4,100
33. 6.4×121.16 ◯ 582
34. 11.68×922 ◯ 11,565
35. 12.1×160 ◯ 2,450
36. $8.8 \times 9{,}290$ ◯ 75,120

Solve.

37. The cargo compartment of a truck is filled with 285 boxes. Each box contains a computer monitor that weighs 18 pounds. Estimate the total weight of the boxes.

    ____

38. A shelf in a computer warehouse contains 75 computer keyboards. Each keyboard weighs 1.55 kg. About how much do the keyboards weigh?

    ____

Practice 24

Name: ____________________

MULTIPLY WHOLE NUMBERS

Multiply. Remember to estimate.

1. 42 × 3

2. $504 × 8

3. 3,018 × 5

4. 5,609 × 8

5. 4,603 × 9

6. 97 × 62

7. 95 × 54

8. 87 × 64

9. $682 × 49

10. 738 × 56

11. 217 × 49

12. $470 × 72

13. $168 × 17

14. 256 × 48

15. 395 × 26

16. 819 × 424

17. 6,850 × 60

18. 497 × 130

19. 2,006 × 38

20. 2,461 × 58

21. 1,025 × 7 ______

22. $308 × 6 ______

23. 24 × 36 ______

24. 293 × 41 ______

25. 486 × 57 ______

26. 674 × 59 ______

27. 908 × 20 ______

28. 351 × 24 ______

29. $137 × 54 ______

30. $317 × 45 ______

31. 6,304 × 67 ______

32. 789 × 6 ______

33. 425 × 21 ______

34. 2,314 × 13 ______

35. 458 × 18 ______

36. 365 × 274 ______

37. 478 × 279 ______

38. 514 × 873 ______

Solve.

39. Each aquarium at the museum contains 265 gallons of water. If there are 6 aquariums, how many gallons of water are there in all the aquariums?

______

40. The aquariums are lighted for 12 hours every day of the year. For how many hours are they lighted each year?

______

Name: ______

Multiply Decimals by Whole Numbers

Multiply. Remember to estimate.

1. 6.9 × 7
2. 3.7 × 6
3. 1.9 × 5
4. 4.9 × 4
5. 7.8 × 3
6. 21.6 × 6
7. 17.2 × 5
8. 41.2 × 9
9. $0.03 × 85
10. 2.07 × 5
11. 178 × 0.04
12. $1.58 × 7
13. 0.891 × 3
14. 208 × 0.9
15. 123 × 0.6
16. 0.367 × 24
17. 0.184 × 41
18. 0.741 × 18
19. 0.417 × 41
20. 0.489 × 20

21. 9 × 1.2 ______
22. 5 × 0.289 ______
23. 21 × $3.01 ______
24. 12 × 1.45 ______
25. 7.73 × 43 ______
26. 5.84 × 61 ______
27. 42.2 × 12 ______
28. $328 × 0.45 ______
29. 30 × 0.6 ______

Multiply mentally.

30. 7 × 60 ______
31. 5 × 9.0 ______
32. 9 × 0.2 ______
33. 0.7 × 200 ______
34. 5 × 0.3 ______
35. 6 × $1.09 ______
36. 300 × 4 ______
37. 7 × 30.0 ______
38. 3 × 3.04 ______

Solve.

39. Sheila earns $0.075 for each newspaper she delivers. If she delivers 54 newspapers a day, how much does she earn each day?

______

40. Kelly earns $25.75 a day working in a record store. If she works 3 nights a week, how much will she earn in one week?

______

Name:

Problem-Solving Strategy: Solve Multistep Problems

✔ Read
✔ Plan
✔ Solve
✔ Look Back

Solve.

1. The Jackson family goes on vacation for a week. Each day they spend $35 on food and $30 on entertainment. How much do they spend on food and entertainment?

2. Arnold spent $3.69 for each roll of film and $4.89 per roll for developing. He took 3 rolls of pictures while on vacation. How much did he spend on his pictures?

3. While on vacation, the Jackson family goes to the gift shop. They buy 2 T-shirts for $14.99 each and 3 mugs for $3.99 each. How much do they spend?

4. The Jacksons rent a car while on vacation. They drive 85 miles a day for a week. If the car rental costs $0.35 a mile, how much do they pay to rent the car for a week?

Solve using any method.
For problems 5–6, use the table and estimate the cost.

5. Two caps and 3 mugs

6. Five postcards, 3 caps, and 2 mugs

SOUVENIRS	
Shirts	$14.99
Caps	$ 5.50
Mugs	$ 3.99
Postcards	$ 0.75

7. **Logical Reasoning** In a footrace, Monique finished 10 seconds behind Angelo. Ryan finished 2 seconds behind Monique. Lian finished 15 seconds ahead of Ryan. In what order did the runners finish?

8. Florida is a popular vacation destination. It has a land area of 58,664 square miles. The state of Georgia has a land area of 58,910 square miles. Which state is larger, and how much larger is it?

Name: ______________________

MULTIPLY DECIMALS BY DECIMALS

Find the product. You may use models to help you multiply.

1. $0.8 \times 0.4 =$ ________ **2.** $0.6 \times 0.7 =$ ________ **3.** $0.5 \times 0.3 =$ ________

4. $0.3 \times 0.9 =$ ________ **5.** $0.3 \times 0.6 =$ ________ **6.** $0.2 \times 0.8 =$ ________

7. $0.8 \times 0.5 =$ ________ **8.** $0.4 \times 0.2 =$ ________ **9.** $0.9 \times 0.8 =$ ________

10. 0.4×0.5 **11.** 0.3×0.2 **12.** 0.7×0.8 **13.** 0.4×0.6 **14.** 0.6×0.9

15. 0.1×0.4 **16.** 0.7×0.3 **17.** 0.5×0.5 **18.** 0.2×0.8 **19.** 0.9×0.9

20. Find the product of 0.4 and 0.9. ______

21. Find the product of 0.1 and 0.5. ______

22. The factors are 0.2 and 0.6. What is the product? ________

23. The factors are 0.3 and 0.8. What is the product? ________

Compare. Write $>$, $<$, or $=$.

24. 0.1×0.5 ◯ 0.6×0.1 **25.** 0.5×0.6 ◯ 0.4×0.7 **26.** 0.3×0.8 ◯ 0.4×0.6

27. 0.8×0.4 ◯ 0.7×0.2 **28.** 0.2×0.8 ◯ 0.4×0.4 **29.** 0.2×0.6 ◯ 0.5×0.9

Solve.

30. Jim walks 0.5 miles to the store. He stops to tie his shoe after walking 0.5 of the total distance. How many miles has he walked?

____

31. At the candy store, a pound of candy costs 90 cents. How much does 0.5 pound of candy cost?

____

Name: ______________________

MULTIPLY DECIMALS

Multiply. Round money amounts to the nearest cent. Remember to estimate.

1. 0.5 × 0.1	**2.** 0.7 × 0.9	**3.** 0.8 × 0.3	**4.** 2.8 × 6.4	**5.** \$6.60 × 7.4
6. 0.18 × 7.6	**7.** 8.7 × 5.3	**8.** 0.25 × 0.2	**9.** \$1.45 × 0.7	**10.** \$1.60 × 0.5
11. \$4.32 × 48.4	**12.** 8.13 × 7.23	**13.** 108 × 65.9	**14.** 5.27 × 2.14	**15.** 0.671 × 2.9
16. 27.83 × 2.49	**17.** 0.713 × 0.219	**18.** \$1.26 × 0.043	**19.** 21.062 × 0.3	**20.** 19.67 × 0.05
21. 0.126 × 3.7	**22.** \$13.95 × 0.02	**23.** 45.189 × 0.7	**24.** 5.85 × 0.23	**25.** 0.0036 × 0.2

26. 0.24 × 0.2 ________ **27.** 6.9 × 2.17 ________ **28.** 0.27 × \$6.47 ________

29. 7.2 × 3.48 ________ **30.** 2.71 × 0.4 ________ **31.** 0.004 × 0.6 ________

32. 0.0065 × 0.3 ________ **33.** 0.1024 × 0.4 ________ **34.** 5.5 × 0.23 ________

35. 4.09 × 4.3 ________ **36.** 2.004 × 2.7 ________ **37.** 4.63 × 2.8 ________

Solve.

38. A school bus uses 0.08 gallons of gasoline for every mile it travels. How many gallons does it use for 18.5 miles?

____

39. A school bus uses 1 gallon of gasoline for every 12.6 miles it travels. How many miles can it travel using 3.4 gallons of gasoline?

____

Name: ______________________________

Problem Solving: Use Underestimates and Overestimates

✔ Read
✔ Plan
✔ Solve
✔ Look Back

Solve. Tell whether you should underestimate or overestimate.

1. Jon is planning a party. He budgets a cost of $3.75 for each of the 12 friends he plans to invite. If he can save $9 a week for 6 weeks, will he have enough?

____

____

____

2. Jon has 3 hours to finish his chores and complete his homework before having his party. Will he have enough time if he spends 1 hour and 40 minutes doing his homework and 30 minutes doing his chores?

____

____

3. Jon wants to give out 5 packs of baseball cards at the party. The cards cost $0.85 a pack. If he plans to spend $5 on the cards, will this be enough?

____

4. Jon wants to make 4 batches of cookies for the party. If each batch costs $2.75, will $12 be enough to cover the cost?

____

____

Solve using any method.

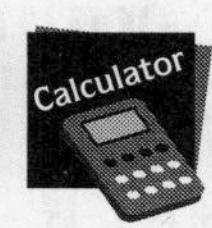

5. Sarah traveled 179 miles to attend a space camp. Her friend traveled 388 miles to get to the camp. How much farther did her friend travel?

____

6. Sarah exercised for 14 hours each week. If she burned 250 calories for every hour of exercise, how many did she burn in one week?

____

7. The length of one year on the planet Pluto is 248.53 times the length of one year on Earth. About how many days is one year on Pluto?

____

____

8. The diameter of Jupiter is about 11 times the diameter of Earth. If the diameter of Earth is 7,926.2 miles, what is the diameter of Jupiter?

____

Name: ______________________________

Mental Math: Estimate Quotients

Divide mentally.

1. 270 ÷ 9 = ________ **2.** 720 ÷ 9 = ________ **3.** 420 ÷ 6 = ________

4. 240 ÷ 8 = ________ **5.** 800 ÷ 4 = ________ **6.** 450 ÷ 9 = ________

7. 6,000 ÷ 2 = ________ **8.** 500 ÷ 50 = ________ **9.** 8,000 ÷ 20 = ________

10. 1,500 ÷ 50 = ________ **11.** 3,600 ÷ 40 = ________ **12.** 1,200 ÷ 30 = ________

13. 5,400 ÷ 60 = ________ **14.** 48,000 ÷ 80 = ________ **15.** 30,000 ÷ 60 = ________

16. 630,000 ÷ 90 = ________ **17.** 8,000 ÷ 200 = ________ **18.** 5,000 ÷ 500 = ________

19. 400)800,000 **20.** 300)270,000 **21.** 4,000)20,000

22. 600)420,000 **23.** 8,000)56,000 **24.** 600)180,000

25. 5,000)35,000 **26.** 3,000)18,000 **27.** 10,000)200,000

28. 7,000)21,000 **29.** 20,000)160,000 **30.** 3,000)240,000

Use compatible numbers to estimate each quotient.

31. 213 ÷ 7 ________ **32.** 364 ÷ 4 ________ **33.** 7,268 ÷ 8 ________

34. 25,403 ÷ 50 ________ **35.** 1,391 ÷ 60 ________ **36.** 1,941 ÷ 70 ________

37. 37,426 ÷ 70 ________ **38.** 49,360 ÷ 83 ________ **39.** 278,013 ÷ 42 ________

Solve.

40. A truck carries 18 boxes. The total weight of the boxes is 6,200 lb. Estimate the weight of each box.

____

41. A manufacturing company produces 49,812 cans. About how many boxes are used if 48 cans are packaged in each box?

____

Name: ______________________

Whole Number Division: 1-Digit Divisors

Divide. Remember to estimate. Do as many as you can mentally.

1. $2\overline{)173}$ **2.** $5\overline{)115}$ **3.** $3\overline{)141}$ **4.** $7\overline{)252}$

5. $6\overline{)4,539}$ **6.** $4\overline{)8,264}$ **7.** $3\overline{)12,989}$ **8.** $5\overline{)82,985}$

9. $412 \div 4 =$ ______ **10.** $250 \div 3 =$ ______ **11.** $334 \div 5 =$ ______

12. $748 \div 7 =$ ______ **13.** $6,048 \div 6 =$ ______ **14.** $2,052 \div 4 =$ ______

15. $4,817 \div 4 =$ ______ **16.** $9,264 \div 5 =$ ______ **17.** $13,209 \div 7 =$ ______

18. $22,212 \div 9 =$ ______ **19.** $15,581 \div 2 =$ ______ **20.** $40,808 \div 8 =$ ______

21. $\frac{628}{6} =$ ______ **22.** $\frac{4,689}{9} =$ ______ **23.** $\frac{2,954}{6} =$ ______

24. $\frac{2,600}{8} =$ ______ **25.** $\frac{24,807}{3} =$ ______ **26.** $\frac{19,111}{2} =$ ______

Algebra Find the missing number mentally.

27. $50 \times$ ______ $= 5,000$ **28.** ______ $\div 20 = 400$ **29.** $6,000 \div 300 =$ ______

30. ______ $\div 8 = 300$ **31.** $9 \times 30 =$ ______ **32.** $540 \div$ ______ $= 9$

33. $4 \times$ ______ $= 2,800$ **34.** $42,000 \div 60 =$ ______ **35.** ______ $\times 70 = 350,000$

36. $800 \times$ ______ $= 64,000$ **37.** $480,000 \div$ ______ $= 800$ **38.** ______ $\div 90 = 800$

Solve.

39. An airplane flew 60,102 miles in one week. What was the average number of miles flown each day that week?

____

40. An airplane flew 2,150 miles in 5 hours. What was the average rate of speed for the airplane in miles per hour?

____

Name: ______________________

Whole Number Division: 2-Digit Divisors

Divide. Remember to estimate.

1. 31)714
2. 21)740
3. 13)868
4. 44)$352
5. 59)2,953
6. 67)2,832
7. 89)7,940
8. 78)2,560
9. 23)18,750
10. 43)21,884
11. 49)$24,500
12. 36)2,163

13. $795 ÷ 53 = ________
14. 648 ÷ 48 = ________
15. 1,148 ÷ 43 = ________
16. $\frac{1,538}{17}$ = ________
17. $\frac{\$1,936}{22}$ = ________
18. 3,550 ÷ 61 = ________
19. 4,366 ÷ 52 = ________
20. 1,166 ÷ 29 = ________
21. $2,460 ÷ 82 = ________
22. 1,938 ÷ 38 = ________
23. 1,470 ÷ 94 = ________
24. 1,984 ÷ 32 = ________

Find the missing number.

	Dividend	Divisor	Quotient
25.	452	2	
27.		3	248 R1
29.	1,366		75 R16

	Dividend	Divisor	Quotient
26.	321		64 R1
28.	2,416	9	
30.		25	32

Solve.

31. A car dealer sold 18,840 cars in one year. Find the average number of cars sold each month.

____

32. A truck dealer sold 29,952 trucks in 4 years. Find the average number of trucks sold each month.

____

Name: ______________________________

Multiplication and Division Expressions

Evaluate each expression.

1. $\frac{a}{6}$ for $a = 96$ ______
2. $3v$ for $v = 5.2$ ______
3. $\frac{c}{5}$ for $c = 135$ ______
4. $17k$ for $k = 3$ ______
5. $\frac{w}{15}$ for $w = 45$ ______
6. $\frac{60}{j}$ for $j = 15$ ______
7. $\frac{b}{24}$ for $b = 48$ ______
8. $50p$ for $p = 9$ ______
9. $\frac{80}{e}$ for $e = 4$ ______
10. $8u$ for $u = 16$ ______
11. $\frac{64}{m}$ for $m = 4$ ______
12. $1.3t$ for $t = 4$ ______
13. $4.6d$ for $d = 2.5$ ______
14. $\frac{y}{32}$ for $y = 480$ ______
15. $\frac{m}{12}$ for $m = 144$ ______

Write an expression for each situation.

16. The number of pieces of mail an office receives each year if the office receives an average of *m* pieces of mail each month

____

17. The number of photocopies that can be made in one minute if a photocopier takes *s* seconds to copy a page

____

18. The cost of each of 25 boxes of paper clips if the total cost is *t* dollars

____

19. The number of phone calls received in 8 hours if an average of *c* calls are received each hour

____

20. The number of yards in a measurement of *z* inches

____

21. The number of months in *y* years

____

Solve.

22. The expression $1{,}250x$ represents the weight of a shipment of 1,250 desk calendars. Suppose each calendar weighs 1.7 pounds. Find the weight of the shipment.

____

23. An office uses approximately *b* reams of paper each day. If the office is open 250 days each year, how many reams of paper are used if they use approximately 2.5 reams a day?

____

Practice 34

Name: ____________________

ORDER OF OPERATIONS

Simplify using order of operations.

1. $22 + (8 \times 2) =$ ________

2. $(35 \div 5) - 5 =$ ________

3. $(200 \div 20) \times 5 =$ ________

4. $40 - (150 \times 0.2) =$ ________

5. $(21 + 4) \times 50 =$ ________

6. $(2.5)^2 - 0.25 =$ ________

7. $(4^3 \div 2) + 10 =$ ________

8. $(250 \times 2) + 23 =$ ________

9. $14 + (10 \div 2) + 3 =$ ________

10. $(4 + 2) \times 3^2 =$ ________

11. $(18 - 3) \div 5 + 9 =$ ________

12. $(10 \div 2) + (9 \times 5) =$ ________

13. $(12 \div 6) \times 3 + 5 =$ ________

14. $(8 \times 3) - (12 \div 4) =$ ________

15. $96 \div (6 \times 2) \div 2 =$ ________

16. $(12 - 4) + (3 \times 2) =$ ________

17. $(5 \times 4) \div 2 + 16 =$ ________

18. $(25 - 20) + (8 \times 9) =$ ________

19. $(9 \times 3) \div (4 + 5) + 8 =$ ________

20. $(8 \times 5) + 5^2 - 3 =$ ________

Evaluate the expression.

21. $72 + 2g$ for $g = 8$ ________

22. $\frac{26}{d} + 11$ for $d = 2$ ________

23. $(18 + 9) \div 3a$ for $a = 3$ ________

24. $(c \div 2) \times 3 + 10$ for $c = 14$ ________

25. $(m^2 \div 4) \times 3$ for $m = 6$ ________

26. $8 + (16 \div 2r)$ for $r = 4$ ________

Solve.

27. Tickets to the school play cost $4.25 for adults and $1.75 for students. If 265 adults and 192 students attended the play, write an expression that shows the amount of money the school made.

____

____

____

28. At the school play, popcorn costs $1 and juice costs 50¢. Suppose 85 people buy popcorn, and 100 people buy juice. Write the expression that shows how much money the school makes by selling refreshments.

____

____

____

Name: ______________________________

Problem-Solving Strategy: Use a Formula

✔ Read
✔ Plan
✔ Solve
✔ Look Back

Solve by using a formula.

1. The distance an automobile travels is given by the formula $d = rt$ where d is distance in miles, r is rate in miles per hour, and t is time in hours. Find the distance an automobile travels at 65 miles per hour for 8.5 hours.

____

2. Using the same formula $d = rt$ to calculate distance traveled, find out how far a bus travels at 40 miles per hour for 6 hours.

____

____

3. The rate of travel is given by the formula $r = \frac{d}{t}$. If a plane completes 900 miles in 1.6 hours, what is its average speed per hour?

____

____

4. The time it takes for a vehicle to travel a certain distance at a certain speed is given by the formula $t = \frac{d}{r}$. How long does it take a motorcycle to get to its destination if it travels 42 miles at a speed of 60 miles an hour?

____

Solve using any method.

5. It took Mylena 1.3 hours to run 10.5 miles in a long-distance race. What was her average speed?

____

____

6. Complete the chart for paper routes.

Kid	Distance	Rate of Travel	Time
Geoff	4 miles	12.5 mph	
Jacqui		14 mph	0.5 hours
Brian	5 miles		0.42 hours
Vijay		13.1 mph	0.4 hours

7. Make a double-line graph from the data table at the right. How much larger was the population of Arizona than Vermont in 1960?

____

____

Population of Two States		
Year	**Arizona**	**Vermont**
1900	120,000	340,000
1930	440,000	360,000
1960	1,300,000	390,000

Name:

Divide Decimals by Whole Numbers

Divide. Remember to estimate.

1. $9\overline{)30.6}$
2. $8\overline{)149.36}$
3. $18\overline{)12.6}$
4. $22\overline{)356.4}$
5. $13\overline{)627.9}$
6. $16\overline{)7{,}828.8}$
7. 5.9 ÷ 2 = ______
8. 38.4 ÷ 3 = ______
9. 22.5 ÷ 15 = ______
10. 19.98 ÷ 18 = ______
11. 386.4 ÷ 16 = ______
12. 1,569.4 ÷ 14 = ______
13. 177.5 ÷ 50 = ______
14. 2,628.85 ÷ 35 = ______
15. 897.92 ÷ 92 = ______
16. $\frac{55.87}{37}$ = ______
17. $\frac{\$452.88}{74}$ = ______
18. $\frac{937.5}{25}$ = ______

Divide. Round to the nearest hundredth or cent, if necessary.

19. $4\overline{)\$3.12}$
20. $12\overline{)73.9}$
21. $23\overline{)13.5}$
22. $6\overline{)11.5}$
23. $2\overline{)\$1.84}$
24. $5\overline{)\$68.25}$
25. $18\overline{)5.76}$
26. $42\overline{)256.76}$
27. $58\overline{)6{,}298.8}$
28. $\frac{\$12.50}{8}$ = ______
29. $\frac{5.45}{40}$ = ______
30. $\frac{\$85.26}{6}$ = ______
31. $\frac{263.41}{7}$ = ______
32. $\frac{213.4}{11}$ = ______
33. $\frac{183.36}{32}$ = ______
34. $\frac{187.42}{12}$ = ______
35. $\frac{\$53.75}{25}$ = ______
36. 942.3 ÷ 26 = ______
37. \$46.44 ÷ 3 = ______
38. \$67.43 ÷ 8 = ______
39. \$9.04 ÷ 16 ______
40. 763.24 ÷ 8 = ______
41. 883.6 ÷ 9 = ______
42. 611.2 ÷ 13 = ______

Name: ____________________

MENTAL MATH: MULTIPLICATION AND DIVISION PATTERNS

Ring the letter of the correct answer.

1. $4.5 \times 100 =$	**a.** 45	**b.** 0.45	**c.** 0.045	**d.** 450
2. $0.82 \div 100 =$	**a.** 0.0082	**b.** 0.082	**c.** 8.2	**d.** 82
3. $17.6 \times 10 =$	**a.** 1,760	**b.** 176	**c.** 1.76	**d.** 0.176
4. $1{,}050.93 \div 1{,}000 =$	**a.** 105.093	**b.** 10.5093	**c.** 1.05093	**d.** 0.105093
5. $0.3 \div 10 =$	**a.** 3	**b.** 30	**c.** 0.03	**d.** 0.003

Find the product or quotient mentally.

6. $13.103 \div 100 =$ ________

7. $4.46 \times 100 =$ ________

8. $1.117 \times 10 =$ ________

9. $1.6 \times 10 =$ ________

10. $12.4 \div 100 =$ ________

11. $0.02 \times 10 =$ ________

12. $9.7 \div 10 =$ ________

13. $0.0064 \times 100 =$ ________

14. $6{,}259 \div 1{,}000 =$ ________

15. $40.2 \times 10 =$ ________

16. $12.652 \times 1{,}000 =$ ________

17. $0.02 \times 100 =$ ________

18. $3.3 \div 10 =$ ________

19. $0.03 \div 100 =$ ________

20. $0.05 \div 10 =$ ________

21. $9.6 \div 100 =$ ________

22. $10.05 \div 1{,}000 =$ ________

23. $2.3 \times 100 =$ ________

24. $0.8 \times 100 =$ ________

25. $27.09 \times 1{,}000 =$ ________

26. $0.48 \div 1{,}000 =$ ________

27. $39.1 \times 1{,}000 =$ ________

28. $7.75 \div 100 =$ ________

29. $1.25 \div 1{,}000 =$ ________

Practice 38

Name:

DIVIDE BY DECIMALS

Find the quotient using the model.

1. 1.5 ÷ 0.5 ________

2. 0.8 ÷ 0.2 ________

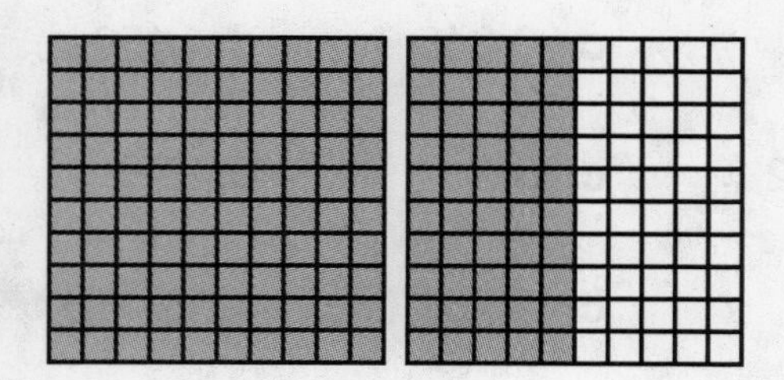

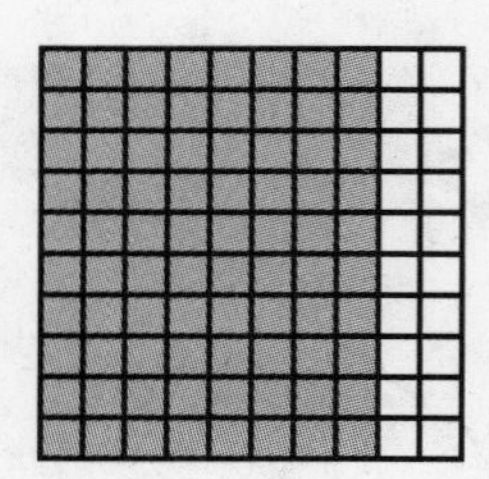

Find the quotient using any method.

3. $0.3\overline{)3.6}$

4. $0.2\overline{)4.4}$

5. $0.8\overline{)10.4}$

6. $0.5\overline{)12.5}$

7. $0.42\overline{)3.78}$

8. $0.62\overline{)5.58}$

9. $0.12\overline{)1.92}$

10. $0.24\overline{)3.36}$

11. $3.2\overline{)9.6}$

12. $0.25\overline{)8}$

13. $0.16\overline{)2.88}$

14. $0.09\overline{)1.35}$

15. 4 ÷ 0.2 = ________

16. 18 ÷ 0.6 = ________

17. 13.5 ÷ 0.9 = ________

18. 6.4 ÷ 0.64 = ________

19. 0.96 ÷ 0.06 = ________

20. 12.8 ÷ 1.6 = ________

21. \$3.12 ÷ \$0.24 = ________

22. 11.7 ÷ 1.3 = ________

23. 0.78 ÷ 0.06 = ________

24. 19.2 ÷ 3.2 = ________

25. 24.3 ÷ 8.1 = ________

26. 7.65 ÷ 0.85 = ________

27. 3.08 ÷ 0.04 = ________

28. 10.4 ÷ 5.2 = ________

29. 6.03 ÷ 0.09 = ________

Name:

DIVIDE BY DECIMALS

Divide. Remember to estimate.

1. $0.4\overline{)6.4}$
2. $0.3\overline{)8.1}$
3. $0.9\overline{)73.8}$
4. $0.8\overline{)41.84}$
5. $0.41\overline{)7.79}$
6. $0.37\overline{)33.67}$
7. $0.75\overline{)11.625}$
8. $0.14\overline{)9.772}$
9. $0.028\overline{)1.036}$
10. $1.5 \div 0.1 =$ ______
11. $36.61 \div 0.7 =$ ______
12. $30.72 \div 0.48 =$ ______
13. $272.34 \div 8.9 =$ ______
14. $1.0809 \div 0.09 =$ ______
15. $1{,}149.5 \div 12.1 =$ ______

Divide. Round the quotient to the nearest hundredth or cent, if necessary.

16. $0.4\overline{)\$0.11}$
17. $0.035\overline{)0.0784}$
18. $1.6\overline{)7.104}$
19. $2.5\overline{)\$8.79}$
20. $1.2\overline{)0.9}$
21. $3.4\overline{)2.14}$
22. $0.55 \div 0.3 =$ ______
23. $6.4 \div 0.9 =$ ______
24. $4.2 \div 1.6 =$ ______
25. $0.9375 \div 0.75 =$ ______
26. $15.537 \div 3.5 =$ ______
27. $\$0.45 \div 0.2 =$ ______
28. $9.756 \div 1.2 =$ ______
29. $5.045 \div 2.5 =$ ______
30. $\$7 \div 9 =$ ______

Solve.

31. Danielle's car uses 15.5 liters of gasoline to travel 375.1 kilometers. What gas mileage does her car get?

______

32. James fills the gasoline tank of his car with 8.5 gallons of gasoline. If he spends $11.89, how much does the gasoline cost for each gallon? Round to the nearest cent.

______

Name: ______________________________

APPLYING MULTIPLICATION AND DIVISION: RELATE METRIC UNITS

Complete.

1. 50 mm = ______ cm **2.** 9 kg = ______ g **3.** 3.7 kL = ______ L

4. 6 L = ______ mL **5.** 0.9 g = ______ mg **6.** 8,200 m = ______ km

7. 2,750 mm = ______ m **8.** 0.015 kL = ______ L **9.** 3.45 g = ______ mg

10. 8.7 L = ______ mL **11.** 35 mg = ______ g **12.** 500 cm = ______ m

13. 185 g = ______ kg **14.** 0.5 cm = ______ m **15.** 1,500 mL = ______ L

16. 7,320 m = ______ km **17.** 0.01 kg = ______ g **18.** 4.25 m = ______ cm

19. 1.84 cm = ______ mm **20.** 30 m = ______ cm **21.** 5,000 L = ______ kL

22. 4,000 mg = ______ g **23.** 0.073 km = ______ m **24.** 0.55 mm = ______ cm

Compare. Write $>$, $<$, or $=$.

25. 600 m ◯ 50 km **26.** 0.3 L ◯ 40 mL **27.** 2,500 mm ◯ 250 cm

28. 2.5 m ◯ 250 cm **29.** 0.008 g ◯ 2 kg **30.** 50 kg ◯ 500 g

31. 200 cm ◯ 20 m **32.** 0.5 km ◯ 50 m **33.** 630 mL ◯ 0.63 L

34. 0.3 km ◯ 30 m **35.** 95 m ◯ 0.095 km **36.** 0.375 L ◯ 3,750 mL

37. 948 mg ◯ 1.5 g **38.** 70 g ◯ 0.007 kg **39.** 0.80 m ◯ 800 cm

Solve.

40. Erin ran in a 10-kilometer race. Matthew ran in a 5,000-meter race. Who ran farther? How much farther?

____

41. Fiona carries a 2-kilogram weight in each of her hands when she walks for exercise. How much weight does she carry in grams?

____

Name: ______________________________

Problem Solving: Interpret Quotients and Remainders

✔ Read
✔ Plan
✔ Solve
✔ Look Back

Solve.

1. Suppose the average length of an automobile is 16 feet. A parking lot measures 145 feet in length. How many automobiles measuring 16 feet in length could park end to end in the lot?

____

2. A car dealership always organizes its cars in rows with equal numbers of cars. There are currently 256 cars in its warehouse, arranged in 32 rows. How many cars are there in each row?

____

3. A carwash can clean up to 4 cars in its machine at one time. On Monday, the carwash cleaned 49 cars. How many times did it operate its machine in all, if 4 cars were always in the machine except for the last time?

____

4. A large truck can carry 12 cars at one time. If a dealership needs to transport 176 cars to its new warehouse at the same time, how many large trucks does it need to have? How many cars will the last truck be carrying, if all the other trucks are full?

____

Solve using any method.

5. An automobile manufacturer uses 2 assembly lines. The first line produces 125 more cars each day than the second line. Together, the lines produce 1,185 cars each day. How many cars does each assembly line produce in one day?

____

____

6. In one year, an assembly line produces 162,500 cars. If there were 260 working days, and the same number of cars was produced each day, how many were produced each day? How many cars would have been produced that year if on half those working days, only half the number of cars were produced?

____

____

Name: ______________________

MENTAL MATH: DIVISIBILITY

Use the divisibility rules to tell whether the number is divisible by 2, 3, 5, 6, 9, or 10.

1. 45 ________ 2. 12 ________ 3. 28 ________ 4. 67 ________

5. 72 ________ 6. 210 ________ 7. 259 ________ 8. 425 ________

9. 388 ________ 10. 702 ________ 11. 5,467 ________ 12. 1,305 ________

13. 3,555 ________ 14. 357,911 ________ 15. 600,435 ________ 16. 4,363,174 ________

17. 25,110 ________ 18. 2,580 ________ 19. 258,003 ________

20. 67,735 ________ 21. 30,630 ________ 22. 198,642 ________

23. 129,340 ________ 24. 5,100,310 ________ 25. 863,975 ________

26. 312,111 ________ 27. 1,002,015 ________ 28. 3,050,100 ________

Use mental math to find the missing digit to make the sentence true. Give all possible answers.

29. 8 ☐,360 is divisible by 9 ________

30. 5 is a factor of 94, ☐ 00 ________

31. 3 is a factor of 3 ☐ 8,962 ________

32. ☐ 0,656 is divisible by 6 ________

33. 630,52 ☐ is divisible by 10 ________

34. 2 is a factor of 123,05 ☐ ________

35. 9 is a factor of 670,12 ☐ ________

36. 133,23 ☐ is divisible by 6 ________

37. 100,3 ☐ 3 is divisible by 3 ________

38. 9,386,13 ☐ is divisible by 2 ________

39. 3 is a factor of 7,654,01 ☐ ________

40. 6,792,32 ☐ is divisible by 3 ________

Solve.

41. Jan's remaining car payments total $2,094. Can she make 6 equal payments? Explain.

____

42. Paolo still needs to repay $636 for a student loan. Can he make 10 equal payments? Explain.

____

Practice 43

Name: ____________

PRIME FACTORIZATION

Tell whether the number is *prime* or *composite*.

1. 13 ________ **2.** 18 ________ **3.** 19 ________

4. 27 ________ **5.** 32 ________ **6.** 37 ________

7. 45 ________ **8.** 56 ________ **9.** 59 ________

10. 79 ________ **11.** 83 ________ **12.** 84 ________

13. 63 ________ **14.** 22 ________ **15.** 29 ________

16. 33 ________ **17.** 17 ________ **18.** 23 ________

19. 46 ________ **20.** 67 ________ **21.** 97 ________

22. 53 ________ **23.** 77 ________ **24.** 39 ________

25. 112 ________ **26.** 101 ________ **27.** 178 ________

Complete the table.

	Number	Prime Factorization
28.	21	
29.	25	
30.		$2 \times 2 \times 2 \times 2 \times 2$
31.		$2 \times 3 \times 7$
32.	56	
33.	68	

	Number	Prime Factorization
34.	74	
35.		$2 \times 2 \times 2 \times 2 \times 5$
36.		5×19
37.	30	
38.	69	
39.	84	

Algebra Find the missing prime factor.

40. $231 = 3 \times 7 \times$ ________

41. $595 = 5 \times$ ________ $\times 17$

42. $1{,}729 = 7 \times$ ________ $\times 19$

43. $150 = 2 \times$ ________ $\times 5 \times 5$

44. $483 = 3 \times 7 \times$ ________

45. $986 =$ ________ $\times 17 \times 29$

46. $1{,}001 = 7 \times$ ________ $\times 13$

47. $2{,}310 = 2 \times$ ________ $\times 5 \times 7 \times 11$

48. $2{,}665 =$ ________ $\times 13 \times 41$

49. $86 = 2 \times$ ________

Name: ____________________

Common Factors and GCF

List all the common factors.

1. 12 and 18 ________ **2.** 9 and 36 ________ **3.** 10 and 50 ________

4. 12 and 16 ________ **5.** 15 and 45 ________ **6.** 11 and 66 ________

7. 6 and 72 ________ **8.** 20 and 64 ________ **9.** 24 and 48 ________

10. 13 and 37 ________ **11.** 14 and 56 ________ **12.** 15 and 85 ________

13. 31 and 62 ________ **14.** 19 and 57 ________ **15.** 8 and 32 ________

16. 28 and 56 ________ **17.** 33 and 99 ________ **18.** 43 and 86 ________

Find the GCF.

19. 9 and 15 ________ **20.** 12 and 24 ________ **21.** 15 and 30 ________

22. 9 and 24 ________ **23.** 12 and 32 ________ **24.** 14 and 42 ________

25. 18 and 48 ________ **26.** 20 and 35 ________ **27.** 24 and 38 ________

28. 16 and 56 ________ **29.** 45 and 54 ________ **30.** 52 and 65 ________

31. 8 and 14 ________ **32.** 9 and 30 ________ **33.** 40 and 64 ________

34. 24 and 50 ________ **35.** 17 and 51 ________ **36.** 14 and 56 ________

Solve.

37. Pam is arranging 16 quarters and 24 dimes on a page in her coin book. She wants to fill the columns with the greatest number of dimes and quarters possible. How should she arrange the page?

____

____

____

38. Pam is arranging 18 nickels and 30 pennies on another page in her coin collection book. She wants to have the same number of rows for the nickels and pennies. How should she arrange them?

____

____

____

Name: ____________________

Common Multiples and LCM

Find the LCM of the numbers.

1. 2 and 7 ________ **2.** 5 and 8 ________ **3.** 3 and 9 ________

4. 4 and 6 ________ **5.** 8 and 10 ________ **6.** 6 and 12 ________

7. 9 and 11 ________ **8.** 10 and 40 ________ **9.** 3 and 12 ________

10. 8 and 9 ________ **11.** 4 and 16 ________ **12.** 5 and 10 ________

13. 3 and 7 ________ **14.** 6 and 8 ________ **15.** 2 and 9 ________

16. 6 and 10 ________ **17.** 9 and 12 ________ **18.** 12 and 16 ________

19. 15 and 25 ________ **20.** 12 and 15 ________ **21.** 32 and 96 ________

22. 20 and 30 ________ **23.** 42 and 84 ________ **24.** 8 and 12 ________

25. 4 and 14 ________ **26.** 14 and 21 ________ **27.** 24 and 36 ________

28. 5 and 12 ________ **29.** 20 and 25 ________ **30.** 2 and 21 ________

31. 16 and 32 ________ **32.** 4 and 25 ________ **33.** 9 and 21 ________

34. 24 and 72 ________ **35.** 45 and 90 ________ **36.** 10 and 14 ________

37. 28 and 32 ________ **38.** 21 and 28 ________ **39.** 21 and 27 ________

40. 16 and 26 ________ **41.** 36 and 54 ________ **42.** 7 and 15 ________

43. 48 and 72 ________ **44.** 6 and 35 ________ **45.** 18 and 60 ________

Solve.

46. A train leaves from track 1 every 20 minutes starting at 10 A.M. A train leaves from track 2 every 45 minutes starting at 10 A.M. How many minutes will pass until trains leave at the same time again?

____

47. An express train leaves every 6 minutes starting at 6 A.M. A local train leaves every 15 minutes starting at 6 A.M. What time will they leave at the same time again?

____

Name: ______________________________

PROBLEM-SOLVING STRATEGY: MAKE AN ORGANIZED LIST

✔ Read
✔ Plan
✔ Solve
✔ Look Back

Solve using the make-an-organized-list strategy. Use the table to solve problems 1–4.

Science	Mathematics	Physical Education
Earth Science	Number Theory	Team Indoor Sports
Space Science	Pre-Algebra	Team Outdoor Sports
	Algebra	Individual Recreational Activities
		Team Recreational Activities

1. Next semester, Imala will choose one science class and one mathematics class. How many different combinations of science and mathematics classes can she choose?

____

2. Rachel will choose one science class and one physical education class. How many different combinations of science and physical education classes can she choose from?

____

3. Jim needs to choose 2 mathematics classes and 2 physical education classes. How many different combinations of those classes can he choose?

____

4. **Write a problem** using information from the table. Solve the problem and then give it to others to solve.

____

Solve using any method.

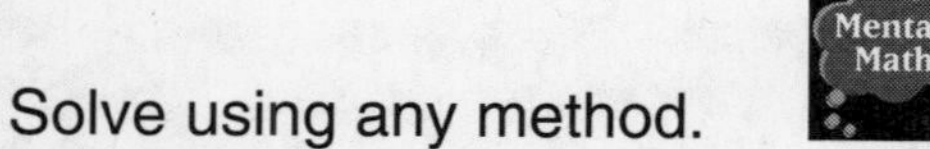

5. A classroom has 16 desks arranged in rows. The same number of desks is in each row. How many different rows of chairs could be in the classroom? What are the options?

____

____

6. A science lab has 6 tables and a capacity of 15 students. Some of the tables seat 2 students, while others seat 3 students. How many tables seating 2 students and how many tables seating 3 students are in the science lab?

____

Practice 47

Name: ____________________

UNDERSTANDING FRACTIONS

Name the fraction shown.

1. 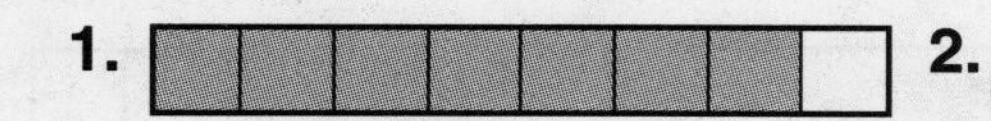

2. 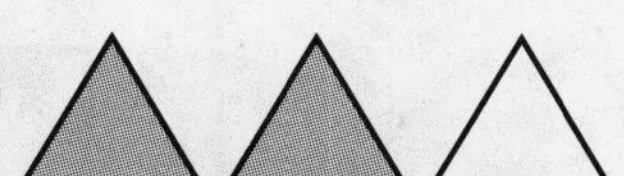

3. 0 $\frac{1}{5}$ $\frac{2}{5}$ $\frac{3}{5}$ $\frac{4}{5}$ $\frac{5}{5}$

4.

5. 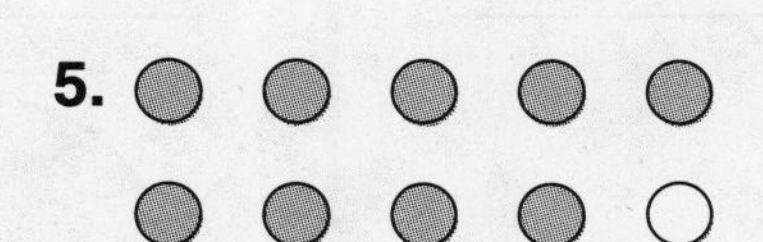

6. 

Make a drawing showing the fraction.

7. $\frac{3}{4}$

8. $\frac{1}{3}$

9. $\frac{3}{5}$

10. $\frac{1}{2}$

11. $\frac{7}{8}$

12. $\frac{9}{16}$

Solve.

13. There are 12 flowers in the arrangement. Six are red, 3 are pink, and 3 are white. What fraction of the flowers are red? pink? white?

14. There are 9 balloons. Two are yellow, 3 are green, and 4 are blue. What fraction of the balloons are yellow, green, and blue?

Name: ______________________

EQUIVALENT FRACTIONS

Does the pair of figures show equivalent fractions? Write *yes* or *no.*

1. 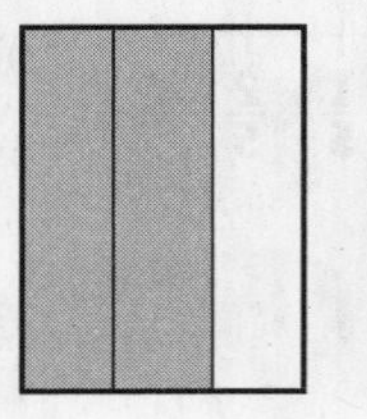

____

2. 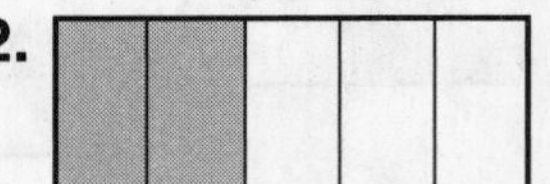

____

3. 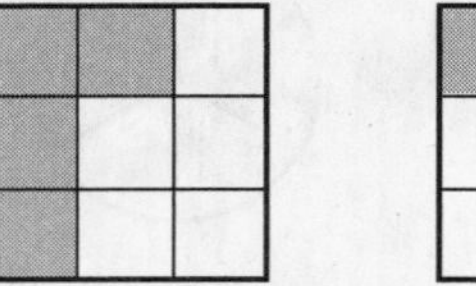

____

4. 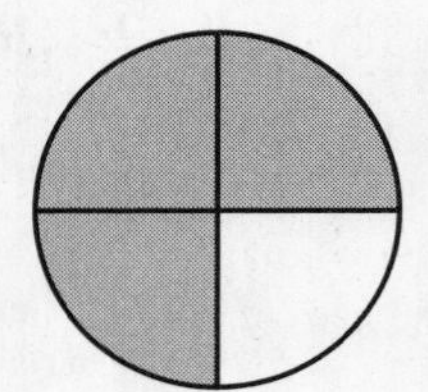 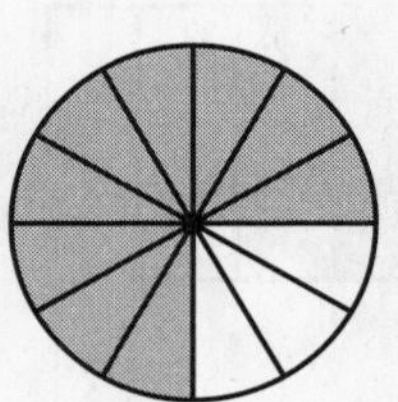

____

Are the fractions equivalent? Write *yes* or *no.*

5. $\frac{3}{4}, \frac{15}{16}$ ______
6. $\frac{5}{6}, \frac{1}{6}$ ______
7. $\frac{7}{21}, \frac{1}{3}$ ______
8. $\frac{4}{10}, \frac{10}{4}$ ______
9. $\frac{2}{9}, \frac{8}{36}$ ______
10. $\frac{3}{8}, \frac{6}{16}$ ______
11. $\frac{5}{10}, \frac{2}{5}$ ______
12. $\frac{12}{20}, \frac{3}{5}$ ______
13. $\frac{14}{18}, \frac{2}{3}$ ______
14. $\frac{7}{10}, \frac{2}{5}$ ______
15. $\frac{5}{12}, \frac{15}{36}$ ______
16. $\frac{1}{18}, \frac{2}{9}$ ______
17. $\frac{1}{5}, \frac{4}{20}$ ______
18. $\frac{5}{8}, \frac{16}{24}$ ______
19. $\frac{3}{4}, \frac{12}{16}$ ______
20. $\frac{7}{12}, \frac{28}{48}$ ______
21. $\frac{4}{7}, \frac{8}{14}$ ______
22. $\frac{2}{9}, \frac{4}{15}$ ______
23. $\frac{2}{3}, \frac{24}{36}$ ______
24. $\frac{7}{12}, \frac{16}{32}$ ______
25. $\frac{3}{8}, \frac{9}{24}$ ______
26. $\frac{5}{12}, \frac{15}{48}$ ______
27. $\frac{2}{7}, \frac{8}{28}$ ______
28. $\frac{8}{9}, \frac{72}{81}$ ______

Write three fractions equivalent to the fraction.

29. $\frac{1}{4}$ ______________
30. $\frac{2}{5}$ ______________
31. $\frac{1}{3}$ ______________
32. $\frac{3}{8}$ ______________
33. $\frac{7}{10}$ ______________
34. $\frac{1}{16}$ ______________
35. $\frac{4}{9}$ ______________
36. $\frac{5}{12}$ ______________
37. $\frac{7}{14}$ ______________

Name: ____________

SIMPLEST FORM

Tell whether the fraction is in simplest form. Write *yes* or *no.*

1. $\frac{5}{10}$ ________ 2. $\frac{2}{3}$ ________ 3. $\frac{9}{12}$ ________ 4. $\frac{6}{8}$ ________ 5. $\frac{2}{9}$ ________

6. $\frac{3}{4}$ ________ 7. $\frac{14}{16}$ ________ 8. $\frac{9}{24}$ ________ 9. $\frac{4}{5}$ ________ 10. $\frac{3}{10}$ ________

11. $\frac{5}{6}$ ________ 12. $\frac{7}{18}$ ________ 13. $\frac{6}{18}$ ________ 14. $\frac{7}{9}$ ________ 15. $\frac{14}{20}$ ________

16. $\frac{2}{8}$ ________ 17. $\frac{3}{7}$ ________ 18. $\frac{2}{6}$ ________ 19. $\frac{5}{15}$ ________ 20. $\frac{3}{5}$ ________

Write the fraction in simplest form. Do as many as you can mentally.

21. $\frac{8}{12}$ ________ 22. $\frac{12}{15}$ ________ 23. $\frac{7}{7}$ ________

24. $\frac{6}{18}$ ________ 25. $\frac{12}{16}$ ________ 26. $\frac{4}{10}$ ________

27. $\frac{20}{24}$ ________ 28. $\frac{10}{40}$ ________ 29. $\frac{14}{20}$ ________

30. $\frac{12}{32}$ ________ 31. $\frac{32}{48}$ ________ 32. $\frac{36}{36}$ ________

33. $\frac{27}{63}$ ________ 34. $\frac{30}{75}$ ________ 35. $\frac{36}{54}$ ________

36. $\frac{25}{60}$ ________ 37. $\frac{50}{80}$ ________ 38. $\frac{44}{66}$ ________

39. $\frac{20}{120}$ ________ 40. $\frac{25}{100}$ ________ 41. $\frac{48}{144}$ ________

42. $\frac{15}{150}$ ________ 43. $\frac{82}{164}$ ________ 44. $\frac{50}{125}$ ________

45. $\frac{96}{128}$ ________ 46. $\frac{42}{64}$ ________ 47. $\frac{33}{96}$ ________

48. $\frac{24}{60}$ ________ 49. $\frac{81}{90}$ ________ 50. $\frac{32}{40}$ ________

51. $\frac{18}{72}$ ________ 52. $\frac{22}{33}$ ________ 53. $\frac{5}{95}$ ________

Name: ____________________

Compare and Order Fractions

Compare. Write >, <, or =.

1. $\frac{2}{5}$ ◯ $\frac{3}{5}$
2. $\frac{7}{16}$ ◯ $\frac{9}{16}$
3. $\frac{5}{8}$ ◯ $\frac{3}{4}$
4. $\frac{1}{8}$ ◯ $\frac{2}{16}$
5. $\frac{1}{3}$ ◯ $\frac{3}{8}$
6. $\frac{3}{8}$ ◯ $\frac{11}{16}$
7. $\frac{1}{6}$ ◯ $\frac{4}{24}$
8. $\frac{3}{10}$ ◯ $\frac{1}{8}$
9. $\frac{10}{12}$ ◯ $\frac{5}{6}$
10. $\frac{1}{4}$ ◯ $\frac{1}{5}$
11. $\frac{2}{3}$ ◯ $\frac{3}{5}$
12. $\frac{16}{28}$ ◯ $\frac{4}{7}$
13. $\frac{1}{2}$ ◯ $\frac{6}{12}$
14. $\frac{7}{8}$ ◯ $\frac{2}{3}$
15. $\frac{3}{5}$ ◯ $\frac{7}{15}$
16. $\frac{11}{15}$ ◯ $\frac{7}{10}$
17. $\frac{5}{8}$ ◯ $\frac{7}{12}$
18. $\frac{9}{10}$ ◯ $\frac{19}{20}$
19. $\frac{7}{10}$ ◯ $\frac{4}{5}$
20. $\frac{5}{12}$ ◯ $\frac{13}{24}$

Order from greatest to least.

21. $\frac{1}{8}, \frac{1}{2}, \frac{1}{4}$ ____________
22. $\frac{3}{8}, \frac{1}{3}, \frac{5}{8}$ ____________
23. $\frac{2}{5}, \frac{7}{10}, \frac{1}{2}$ ____________
24. $\frac{5}{6}, \frac{3}{4}, \frac{5}{8}$ ____________
25. $\frac{1}{2}, \frac{3}{4}, \frac{2}{5}$ ____________
26. $\frac{5}{6}, \frac{3}{5}, \frac{7}{10}$ ____________
27. $\frac{3}{16}, \frac{1}{8}, \frac{1}{4}$ ____________
28. $\frac{5}{8}, \frac{7}{12}, \frac{3}{4}$ ____________
29. $\frac{9}{16}, \frac{1}{2}, \frac{2}{3}$ ____________
30. $\frac{7}{8}, \frac{2}{5}, \frac{1}{3}$ ____________
31. $\frac{11}{12}, \frac{4}{7}, \frac{5}{9}$ ____________
32. $\frac{7}{8}, \frac{2}{9}, \frac{3}{4}$ ____________
33. $\frac{8}{11}, \frac{5}{12}, \frac{3}{5}$ ____________
34. $\frac{4}{9}, \frac{5}{7}, \frac{3}{8}$ ____________

Solve. Use the table for problem 35.

35. Which candidate received the most votes? What fraction of the votes cast did that candidate receive?

____

VOTES FOR CLASS PRESIDENT			
Grade	C. Andreas	J. Johnson	R. Vargas
6	3	12	6
7	14	5	7
8	4	2	13

Practice 51

Name: ______________________

UNDERSTANDING MIXED NUMBERS

Write the mixed number.

1. 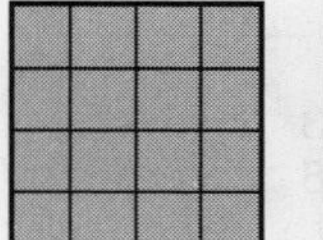 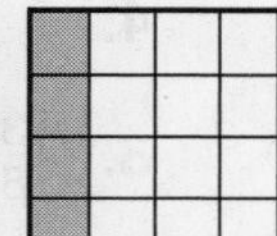

____

2. 

____

3. 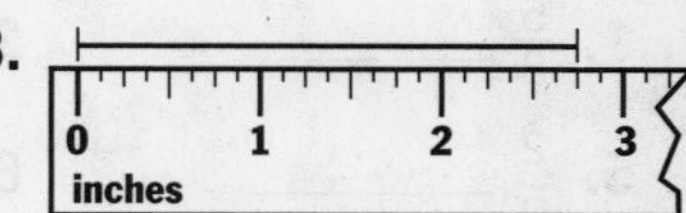

____

Complete.

	Whole or Mixed Number	Improper Fraction
4.		$\frac{8}{3}$
5.		$\frac{9}{7}$
6.		$\frac{28}{4}$
7.		$\frac{35}{8}$
8.		$\frac{19}{5}$
9.		$\frac{25}{4}$
10.		$\frac{36}{6}$

	Whole or Mixed Number	Improper Fraction
11.		$\frac{46}{5}$
12.		$\frac{53}{8}$
13.		$\frac{17}{3}$
14.		$\frac{11}{8}$
15.		$\frac{14}{5}$
16.	$10\frac{3}{4}$	
17.	$3\frac{1}{3}$	

	Whole or Mixed Number	Improper Fraction
18.	16	
19.	$12\frac{2}{3}$	
20.	$17\frac{1}{4}$	
21.	$21\frac{1}{2}$	
22.	$3\frac{9}{10}$	
23.	$14\frac{1}{3}$	
24.	$20\frac{4}{5}$	

Solve.

25. Lori is 5 feet $4\frac{1}{2}$ inches tall. Her twin brother Richard is 5 feet $5\frac{1}{4}$ inches tall. Who is taller?

____

26. Richard's dog weighs 34 pounds. Lori's dog weighs $32\frac{1}{2}$ pounds. Which dog weighs the least?

____

Name: ______________________

Connect Fractions, Mixed Numbers, and Decimals

Write as a decimal. Round the decimal to the nearest hundredth if necessary.

1. $\frac{5}{8}$ ________ **2.** $\frac{1}{3}$ ________ **3.** $\frac{7}{10}$ ________ **4.** $\frac{1}{6}$ ________

5. $\frac{2}{5}$ ________ **6.** $3\frac{3}{4}$ ________ **7.** $5\frac{4}{5}$ ________ **8.** $2\frac{3}{8}$ ________

9. $3\frac{3}{10}$ ________ **10.** $4\frac{1}{8}$ ________ **11.** $10\frac{7}{20}$ ________ **12.** $13\frac{7}{8}$ ________

13. $16\frac{1}{4}$ ________ **14.** $11\frac{12}{25}$ ________ **15.** $20\frac{3}{16}$ ________ **16.** $12\frac{4}{5}$ ________

17. $9\frac{7}{8}$ ________ **18.** $22\frac{1}{2}$ ________ **19.** $19\frac{3}{4}$ ________ **20.** $14\frac{8}{9}$ ________

21. $6\frac{3}{5}$ ________ **22.** $18\frac{1}{9}$ ________ **23.** $2\frac{1}{4}$ ________ **24.** $3\frac{3}{8}$ ________

25. $21\frac{4}{7}$ ________ **26.** $17\frac{2}{3}$ ________ **27.** $4\frac{7}{16}$ ________ **28.** $6\frac{9}{11}$ ________

29. $3\frac{9}{16}$ ________ **30.** $22\frac{1}{5}$ ________ **31.** $7\frac{6}{7}$ ________ **32.** $4\frac{1}{3}$ ________

Write as a fraction or mixed number in simplest form.

33. 0.2 ________ **34.** 0.9 ________ **35.** 0.1 ________ **36.** 0.55 ________

37. 0.72 ________ **38.** 0.02 ________ **39.** 4.5 ________ **40.** 5.37 ________

41. 2.25 ________ **42.** 9.4 ________ **43.** 8.625 ________ **44.** 3.45 ________

45. 30.875 ________ **46.** 25.68 ________ **47.** 12.495 ________ **48.** 19.8 ________

49. 3.17 ________ **50.** 34.4 ________ **51.** 61.65 ________ **52.** 16.675 ________

53. 2.44 ________ **54.** 6.93 ________ **55.** 7.65 ________ **56.** 3.305 ________

57. 0.675 ________ **58.** 10.25 ________ **59.** 32.875 ________ **60.** 0.56 ________

61. 3.48 ________ **62.** 56.012 ________ **63.** 0.018 ________ **64.** 4.75 ________

Name:

PROBLEM SOLVING: EXPRESS QUOTIENTS

✔ Read
✔ Plan
✔ Solve
✔ Look Back

Solve. Use the table for problems 1–4.

MONEY EARNED BY CLASS			
	Grade 6	Grade 7	Grade 8
Number of Students	24	28	25
Amount Earned	$198.00	$212.80	$406.25

1. What was the average amount earned by each student in Grade 6, in Grade 7, and in Grade 8?

2. The eighth graders conducted a fundraiser to raise money. If the students were stationed in rows of 6 at phones, how many rows will they fill completely? How many students will be in the last row?

3. About what fraction of the total money did Grade 7 raise? Grade 8?

4. The school wants to raise $900. About what fraction of the money have they earned so far? About how much more in dollars do they need?

Solve using any method.

5. The Hillside Pep Band needs $1,200 for new uniforms. They raised $75 the first week. If the band raises the same amount of money each week, how many more weeks do they need?

6. If the band wants to buy 36 uniforms for $1,200, about how much does each uniform cost?

7. Laura and Len work at the cafeteria. Laura has every fifth day off, and Len has every sixth day off. If they both have a day off today, how many days will it be until they are off again on the same day?

8. Juan and Ella work together at a carwash. Juan has every third day off, and Ella has every fourth and fifth day off. If they both have a day off today, how many days will it be until they are off again on the same day?

Name: ____________________

Estimate Sums and Differences

Round to the nearest half.

1. $10\frac{2}{5}$ ______
2. $7\frac{4}{5}$ ______
3. $2\frac{7}{12}$ ______
4. $9\frac{2}{3}$ ______
5. $12\frac{2}{15}$ ______
6. $6\frac{4}{7}$ ______
7. $15\frac{1}{8}$ ______
8. $16\frac{5}{8}$ ______
9. $8\frac{9}{10}$ ______
10. $5\frac{3}{16}$ ______
11. $2\frac{5}{12}$ ______
12. $7\frac{7}{10}$ ______
13. $4\frac{4}{5}$ ______
14. $3\frac{3}{8}$ ______
15. $1\frac{1}{3}$ ______
16. $4\frac{17}{20}$ ______
17. $7\frac{9}{16}$ ______
18. $12\frac{1}{12}$ ______
19. $6\frac{7}{16}$ ______
20. $8\frac{13}{15}$ ______

Estimate each sum or difference.

21. $10\frac{2}{3} - \frac{5}{6}$ ______
22. $5\frac{3}{8} + 2\frac{7}{10}$ ______
23. $4\frac{1}{5} - 3\frac{4}{9}$ ______
24. $\frac{7}{12} + 13\frac{8}{9}$ ______
25. $8\frac{5}{8} - 8\frac{1}{12}$ ______
26. $\frac{13}{14} + \frac{1}{7}$ ______
27. $11\frac{5}{12} + 1\frac{3}{5}$ ______
28. $24\frac{1}{3} - 17\frac{7}{16}$ ______
29. $14\frac{1}{6} - 11\frac{5}{8}$ ______
30. $3\frac{1}{2} + 3\frac{7}{8}$ ______
31. $2\frac{5}{6} + 1\frac{1}{5} + 6$ ______
32. $7 + \frac{2}{6} + 1\frac{6}{9}$ ______
33. $5 + 2\frac{5}{8} + 4$ ______
34. $3\frac{7}{10} + 1\frac{1}{4} + 6\frac{11}{20}$ ______
35. $3\frac{11}{12} + 5\frac{1}{4} + 1\frac{11}{30}$ ______

Solve.

36. In a woodworking class, 13 out of 16 students check their computation using a calculator. Do few, about half, or most students use a calculator to check their computations?

____

37. Sara used $\frac{3}{5}$ of a container of paint to paint her bedroom door. She used $3\frac{1}{2}$ containers of paint to paint her walls. About how much paint did she use?

____

Name: ______________________________

Practice 55

ADD AND SUBTRACT LIKE FRACTIONS

Add or subtract. Write the answer in simplest form.

1. $\frac{1}{4} + \frac{3}{4}$ ______ **2.** $\frac{7}{16} + \frac{5}{16}$ ______ **3.** $\frac{1}{3} + \frac{1}{3}$ ______

4. $\frac{3}{8} + \frac{7}{8}$ ______ **5.** $\frac{9}{10} - \frac{7}{10}$ ______ **6.** $\frac{4}{7} - \frac{1}{7}$ ______

7. $\frac{1}{8} + \frac{7}{8} + \frac{5}{8}$ ______ **8.** $\frac{9}{16} + \frac{3}{16} + \frac{5}{16}$ ______

9. $\frac{1}{3} + \frac{2}{3}$

10. $\frac{4}{5} - \frac{2}{5}$

11. $\frac{9}{10} - \frac{5}{10}$

12. $\frac{11}{12} - \frac{1}{12}$

13. $\frac{5}{8} + \frac{7}{8} + \frac{3}{8}$

14. $\frac{2}{5} + \frac{4}{5} + \frac{3}{5}$

15. $\frac{11}{12} + \frac{5}{12} + \frac{1}{12}$

16. $\frac{2}{9} + \frac{4}{9} + \frac{7}{9}$

Algebra Find the missing number.

17. $\frac{1}{4} + \frac{3}{4} = \frac{\square}{4}$ **18.** $\frac{4}{10} - \frac{\square}{10} = \frac{3}{10}$ **19.** $\frac{\square}{8} + \frac{1}{8} = \frac{4}{8}$

20. $\frac{13}{15} - \frac{\square}{15} = \frac{8}{15}$ **21.** $\frac{\square}{7} + \frac{4}{7} = \frac{11}{7}$ **22.** $\frac{8}{9} - \frac{2}{9} = \frac{\square}{9}$

Solve.

23. On days when Arturo does not have soccer practice, he jogs $\frac{7}{10}$ mile before school and $\frac{9}{10}$ mile after school. How far does he jog?

____

24. It took Karl $\frac{3}{4}$ of an hour to do his homework. If his math homework took $\frac{1}{4}$ of an hour, how much time did the rest of his homework take?

____

Name: ____________________

Add Unlike Fractions

Add. Write the answer in simplest form. Remember to estimate.

1. $\frac{1}{2} + \frac{3}{4}$

2. $\frac{2}{3} + \frac{4}{5}$

3. $\frac{3}{16} + \frac{5}{8}$

4. $\frac{5}{6} + \frac{1}{3}$

5. $\frac{1}{6} + \frac{5}{12}$

6. $\frac{7}{16} + \frac{18}{32}$

7. $\frac{8}{15} + \frac{1}{3}$

8. $\frac{1}{8} + \frac{1}{4}$

9. $\frac{1}{3} + \frac{3}{4}$

10. $\frac{5}{8} + \frac{11}{32}$

11. $\frac{15}{16} + \frac{1}{8}$

12. $\frac{2}{3} + \frac{7}{10}$

13. $\frac{3}{5} + \frac{3}{4}$ ______

14. $\frac{5}{6} + \frac{1}{3}$ ______

15. $\frac{13}{16} + \frac{1}{2}$ ______

16. $\frac{1}{3} + \frac{4}{7}$ ______

17. $\frac{1}{4} + \frac{4}{7}$ ______

18. $\frac{3}{4} + \frac{5}{6}$ ______

19. $\frac{8}{15} + \frac{2}{5}$ ______

20. $\frac{1}{6} + \frac{11}{15}$ ______

21. $\frac{5}{6} + \frac{7}{18} + \frac{2}{3}$ ______

22. $\frac{1}{2} + \frac{1}{4} + \frac{11}{16}$ ______

23. $\frac{4}{9} + \frac{1}{3} + \frac{5}{6}$ ______

24. $\frac{1}{2} + \frac{3}{10} + \frac{2}{5}$ ______

The circle graph shows the hair color of all the students in Ms. Lemke's mathematics class. Use the graph to solve each problem.

25. What fraction of the class has either black or brown hair?

____

26. What fraction of the class does not have red hair?

____

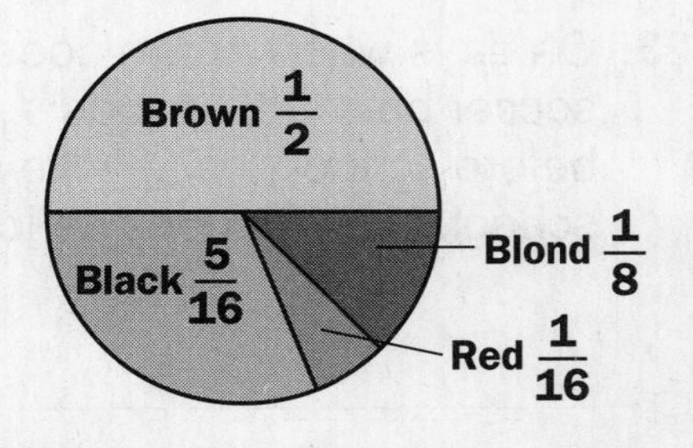

Name: ____________________

SUBTRACT UNLIKE FRACTIONS

Subtract. Write the answer in simplest form. Remember to estimate.

1. $\frac{1}{2} - \frac{3}{8}$

2. $\frac{11}{12} - \frac{3}{4}$

3. $\frac{4}{9} - \frac{1}{3}$

4. $\frac{6}{7} - \frac{1}{2}$

5. $\frac{3}{4} - \frac{3}{10}$

6. $\frac{2}{3} - \frac{5}{12}$

7. $\frac{2}{3} - \frac{3}{5}$

8. $\frac{5}{6} - \frac{3}{4}$

9. $\frac{5}{6} - \frac{1}{5}$

10. $\frac{5}{6} - \frac{1}{12}$

11. $\frac{3}{4} - \frac{1}{6}$

12. $\frac{5}{12} - \frac{1}{6}$

13. $\frac{4}{7} - \frac{5}{14}$ ______

14. $\frac{17}{24} - \frac{7}{12}$ ______

15. $\frac{7}{12} - \frac{2}{9}$ ______

16. $\frac{11}{12} - \frac{9}{10}$ ______

17. $\frac{2}{3} - \frac{1}{9}$ ______

18. $\frac{3}{10} - \frac{1}{5}$ ______

19. $\frac{3}{4} - \frac{1}{3}$ ______

20. $\frac{2}{3} - \frac{1}{2}$ ______

Algebra Simplify using order of operation rules.

21. $\frac{3}{4} - \frac{1}{2} - \frac{1}{6}$ ______

22. $\frac{7}{8} + \frac{1}{3} - \frac{5}{12}$ ______

23. $\frac{2}{3} - \frac{3}{5} + \frac{7}{15}$ ______

Solve.

24. Jeremy played tennis for $\frac{3}{4}$ hour on Saturday and $\frac{2}{3}$ hour on Sunday. How much longer did he play on Saturday than on Sunday?

____

25. Amy walked $\frac{1}{2}$ mile on the track. Then she jogged the next $\frac{3}{10}$ mile. How much further did she walk than jog?

____

Name: ______________________________

ADD MIXED NUMBERS

Add, using any method. Write the answer in simplest form.

1. $1\frac{3}{4} + 4\frac{1}{4}$
2. $5\frac{5}{6} + 7\frac{1}{3}$
3. $2\frac{7}{10} + 8\frac{2}{5}$
4. $10\frac{9}{16} + 6\frac{7}{16}$
5. $\frac{1}{2} + 3\frac{2}{3}$
6. $9\frac{3}{10} + 8\frac{1}{2}$
7. $5\frac{1}{2} + 1\frac{5}{8}$
8. $9\frac{1}{2} + 6\frac{1}{2}$
9. $2\frac{1}{6} + 1\frac{7}{12}$
10. $4\frac{2}{3} + 4\frac{5}{6}$
11. $7\frac{4}{9} + \frac{2}{3}$
12. $2\frac{1}{6} + 5\frac{1}{2}$
13. $8\frac{3}{8} + 8\frac{2}{3}$
14. $\frac{3}{5} + 4\frac{4}{15}$
15. $3\frac{3}{4} + 10\frac{1}{6}$

16. $6\frac{1}{6} + 5\frac{5}{12}$ ______
17. $1\frac{5}{8} + 14\frac{7}{8}$ ______
18. $3\frac{7}{12} + 5\frac{2}{3}$ ______
19. $2\frac{1}{2} + 4\frac{1}{3}$ ______
20. $3\frac{7}{12} + \frac{11}{12}$ ______
21. $2 + 2\frac{1}{6}$ ______
22. $7\frac{4}{5} + 4\frac{3}{25}$ ______
23. $5\frac{5}{6} + 6\frac{3}{4}$ ______
24. $4\frac{5}{6} + 2\frac{2}{5}$ ______
25. $4\frac{9}{10} + 7\frac{2}{5}$ ______
26. $7\frac{5}{6} + 2\frac{1}{3}$ ______
27. $5\frac{5}{12} + 2\frac{2}{3}$ ______

Solve.

28. Lori rode her bike $1\frac{1}{10}$ miles to her friend's house. Her trip home was $1\frac{2}{5}$ miles because she stopped at the store. How far did Lori ride her bike?

____

29. Dan walked $4\frac{1}{2}$ blocks from school to the pool and then another $3\frac{3}{4}$ blocks to his home. How far did he walk?

____

Name: ______________________

ADD MIXED NUMBERS

Add. Write the answer in simplest form. Remember to estimate.

1. $2\frac{4}{5} + 1\frac{1}{5}$

2. $5\frac{2}{3} + 8\frac{5}{6}$

3. $3\frac{1}{4} + 6\frac{3}{8}$

4. $\frac{7}{10} + 2\frac{1}{5}$

5. $7\frac{5}{6} + 4\frac{5}{6}$

6. $1 + 9\frac{2}{3}$

7. $4\frac{1}{2} + 6\frac{9}{10}$

8. $7\frac{7}{8} + 1\frac{11}{12}$

9. $5\frac{1}{5} + 2\frac{1}{3}$ ______

10. $3\frac{4}{5} + 7\frac{3}{5}$ ______

11. $7\frac{1}{4} + 4\frac{3}{10} + 2\frac{3}{5}$ ______

12. $1\frac{5}{12} + 6\frac{1}{4}$ ______

13. $5\frac{3}{8} + 6\frac{11}{12}$ ______

14. $8\frac{1}{8} + 2\frac{3}{4} + 3\frac{1}{2}$ ______

Algebra Evaluate each expression.

15. $x + \frac{3}{4}$ for $x = 4\frac{1}{2}$ ______

16. $3\frac{5}{6} + y$ for $y = 9\frac{1}{8}$ ______

17. $a + 6\frac{4}{7}$ for $a = \frac{5}{14}$ ______

18. $2\frac{15}{16} + n$ for $n = 10\frac{5}{8}$ ______

19. $m + 2\frac{1}{10}$ for $m = 4\frac{3}{5}$ ______

20. $8\frac{9}{10} + c$ for $c = 3\frac{2}{5}$ ______

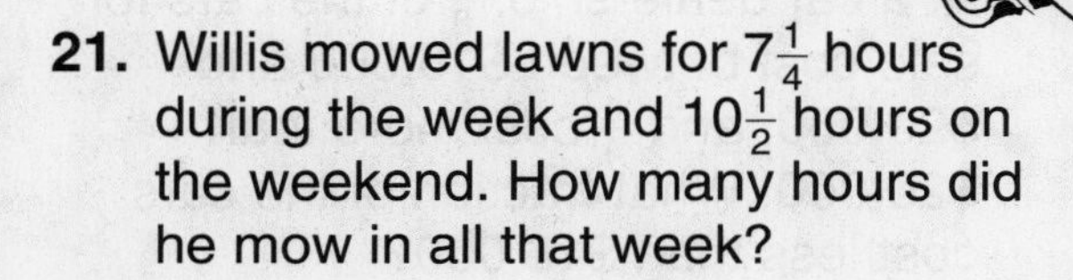

Solve.

21. Willis mowed lawns for $7\frac{1}{4}$ hours during the week and $10\frac{1}{2}$ hours on the weekend. How many hours did he mow in all that week?

____

22. To earn extra money Willis also tutored math on Wednesdays for $1\frac{1}{2}$ hours and Fridays for $\frac{2}{3}$ hour. How many hours did Willis tutor?

____

Name: ____________________

Problem-Solving Strategy: Find a Pattern

✔ Read
✔ Plan
✔ Solve
✔ Look Back

Solve by finding a pattern.

1. Look at the pattern of dots shown below. First 1 dot is shown, then 4 dots, and so on. How many dots would be shown sixth in the pattern? Describe how you found your answer.

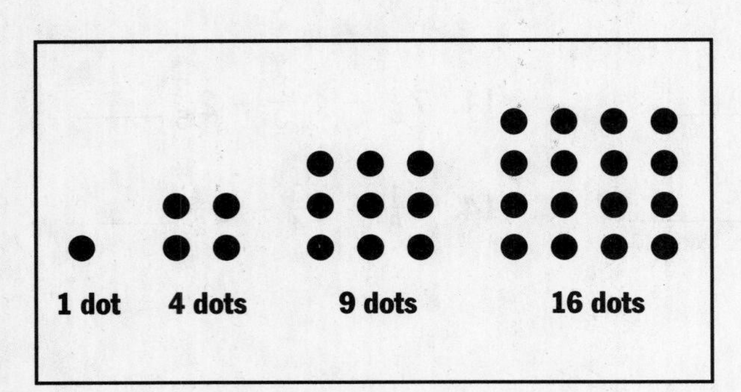

2. Write the next fraction and describe the pattern you used.

$\frac{1}{4}, \frac{5}{16}, \frac{3}{8}, \frac{7}{16}, \frac{1}{2}, \frac{9}{16}, \ldots$

3. Frank loaded $2\frac{1}{2}$ cartons of batteries in 5 minutes, $3\frac{1}{4}$ cartons in the next 10 minutes, and 4 cartons in the next 15 minutes. If this pattern continues, how many cartons will he load in the next 20 minutes?

4. Supersavers sells 2 flashlights for \$5.99, 3 for \$8.74, 4 for \$11.49, and 5 for \$14.24. If this pattern continues, how much will it cost to buy 8 flashlights?

Solve using any method.

5. If Pierre walks at an average speed of $4\frac{1}{2}$ miles per hour, how far could he walk in 3 hours?

6. At a car dealership, $\frac{3}{8}$ of the cars for sale cost between \$16,000 and \$20,000, and $\frac{1}{4}$ cost more than \$20,000. What fraction of the cars cost less than \$16,000?

Name: ______________________

SUBTRACT MIXED NUMBERS

Subtract, using any method. Write the answer in simplest form.

1. $7\frac{3}{4} - 1\frac{1}{4}$

2. $15\frac{7}{12} - 6\frac{11}{12}$

3. $4\frac{1}{3} - 2$

4. $9\frac{1}{6} - 5\frac{2}{3}$

5. $7\frac{1}{5} - \frac{1}{3}$

6. $10\frac{1}{10} - 6\frac{7}{10}$

7. $3 - \frac{2}{3}$

8. $10\frac{5}{8} - 9\frac{3}{4}$

9. $11\frac{3}{5} - 8\frac{1}{10}$

10. $12 - 8\frac{3}{4}$

11. $4\frac{1}{2} - 3\frac{3}{8}$

12. $1\frac{4}{5} - 1\frac{1}{2}$

13. $1 - \frac{3}{5}$ ______

14. $14\frac{1}{4} - 3\frac{3}{4}$ ______

15. $5\frac{5}{12} - 1\frac{11}{12}$ ______

16. $18\frac{5}{12} - 4\frac{7}{12}$ ______

17. $18 - 7\frac{3}{10}$ ______

18. $15\frac{1}{4} - 2\frac{5}{8}$ ______

19. $6\frac{5}{8} - 4$ ______

20. $9\frac{1}{3} - 8\frac{1}{2}$ ______

21. $13\frac{1}{2} - 10\frac{1}{3}$ ______

22. $16\frac{2}{3} - 12\frac{1}{6}$ ______

23. $14\frac{3}{8} - 12\frac{1}{2}$ ______

24. $8\frac{2}{3} - 5\frac{11}{12}$ ______

Solve.

25. Ruben weighed $7\frac{3}{4}$ pounds when he was born. On his first birthday, he weighed $21\frac{1}{2}$ pounds. How much weight did Ruben gain his first year?

____

26. Zhing is 68 inches tall. Her brother Hao is $65\frac{3}{4}$ inches tall. How much taller is Zhing than Hao?

____

Name: ____________________

SUBTRACT MIXED NUMBERS

Subtract. Write the answer in simplest form. Remember to estimate.

1. $11\frac{5}{8} - 2\frac{7}{8}$

2. $10\frac{3}{4} - 6\frac{1}{8}$

3. $10\frac{1}{10} - 6\frac{7}{10}$

4. $4\frac{1}{6} - 3\frac{1}{2}$

5. $6\frac{3}{4} - 4\frac{7}{8}$

6. $14\frac{1}{2} - \frac{5}{6}$

7. $16 - \frac{5}{12}$

8. $3\frac{14}{15} - 3\frac{4}{5}$

9. $9\frac{7}{10} - 9\frac{2}{5}$ ______

10. $11\frac{2}{3} - 3\frac{4}{5}$ ______

11. $5\frac{7}{8} - 2\frac{1}{6}$ ______

12. $15\frac{1}{3} - 9\frac{3}{5}$ ______

13. $13\frac{11}{15} - \frac{7}{10}$ ______

14. $7 - 4\frac{3}{5}$ ______

Add or subtract mentally.

15. $2 + 4\frac{1}{3}$ ______

16. $8\frac{1}{8} - 5$ ______

17. $3\frac{1}{4} + 4\frac{1}{4}$ ______

18. $6 - 2\frac{1}{4}$ ______

19. $9\frac{5}{8} - 4\frac{3}{8}$ ______

20. $2\frac{1}{3} + 3\frac{1}{3} + 4\frac{1}{3}$ ______

21. $5\frac{1}{2} - 2\frac{1}{2}$ ______

22. $1\frac{1}{4} + 3\frac{1}{2}$ ______

23. $6\frac{1}{2} + 2\frac{1}{2}$ ______

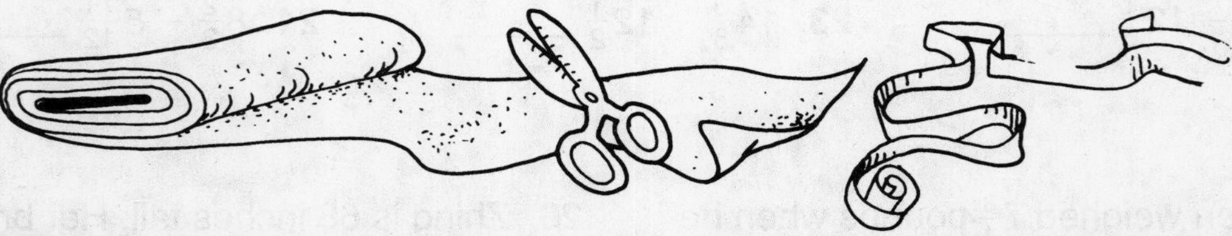

Solve.

24. Robert bought 3 yards of material to make a banner. If he uses $2\frac{1}{6}$ yards, how much will he have left?

____

25. Robert's mother has $4\frac{2}{3}$ yards of ribbon. She needs $1\frac{3}{4}$ yards. How much ribbon is left to give to Robert?

____

Name:

Practice 63

PROBLEM SOLVING: FIND NEEDED OR EXTRA INFORMATION

✔ Read
✔ Plan
✔ Solve
✔ Look Back

Solve. If there is not enough information, identify the information you need, estimate what it should be, and then solve.

1. Sydney has 47 compact discs. The thickness of a compact disc case is $\frac{7}{16}$ inch. If 3 compact disc cases are stacked vertically, how tall is the stack? What information is not needed?

2. A class of 130 students and 5 adults are planning to go to a concert. How many school buses will be needed to carry the group?

3. Aaron is less than 20 years old. His friend Carla is 14. Aaron's exact age is a multiple of 4, 6, and 12. How old is Aaron? What information is not needed?

4. Derek bought 3 cartons of juice for \$2.69 each and 2 half gallons of milk. How much did he spend?

Solve using any method.

5. At a car wash, 18 cars were washed and 4 were waxed. How much money was raised if the cost of a wash was \$1.75 and the cost of a wax was \$4.50?

6. Roberto practices the piano for 45 minutes each day. In simplest form, what fraction of an hour does Roberto practice each day?

7. **Logical Reasoning** One day, a music teacher shakes hands with each of his 8 students, then asks each student to shake hands once with every other student. How many handshakes occurred on that day?

8. A coin bank contains twice as many nickels as dimes and $\frac{1}{3}$ as many quarters as dimes. How many nickels, dimes, and quarters are in the bank if the bank contains \$1.70?

Name: ______________________________

Mental Math: Find a Fraction of a Whole Number

Multiply mentally.

1. $\frac{3}{4}$ of 12 ____ 2. $\frac{2}{5}$ of 20 ____ 3. $\frac{1}{2}$ of 22 ____ 4. $\frac{5}{7}$ of 21 ____

5. $\frac{7}{8} \times 32$ ____ 6. $\frac{4}{9} \times 45$ ____ 7. $\frac{2}{3} \times 33$ ____ 8. $\frac{3}{5} \times 10$ ____

9. $\frac{1}{4} \times 20$ ____ 10. $\frac{3}{10} \times 50$ ____ 11. $\frac{1}{9} \times 45$ ____ 12. $\frac{2}{9} \times 54$ ____

13. $\frac{3}{5}$ of 55 ____ 14. $\frac{5}{8}$ of 64 ____ 15. $\frac{2}{7}$ of 84 ____ 16. $\frac{5}{6}$ of 72 ____

17. $\frac{1}{8} \times 80$ ____ 18. $\frac{1}{2} \times 30$ ____ 19. $\frac{3}{8} \times 96$ ____ 20. $\frac{1}{3} \times 90$ ____

21. $\frac{2}{3}$ of 120 ____ 22. $\frac{7}{9}$ of 810 ____ 23. $\frac{4}{5}$ of 150 ____ 24. $\frac{9}{10}$ of 200 ____

25. 1 foot = 12 inches
 $\frac{3}{4}$ feet = ____ inches

26. 1 pound = 16 ounces
 $\frac{3}{8}$ pound = ____ ounces

27. 1 yard = 36 inches
 $\frac{1}{4}$ yard = ____ inches

28. 1 quart = 32 ounces
 $\frac{1}{2}$ quart = ____ ounces

29. 1 minute = 60 seconds
 $\frac{1}{10}$ minute = ____ seconds

30. 1 yd = 36 inches
 $\frac{5}{6}$ yd = ____ inches

Algebra Find the missing number.

31. $\frac{1}{2} \times$ ____ = 9 32. ____ of 33 = 11 33. $\frac{3}{8} \times 24 =$ ____ 34. $\frac{1}{10}$ of ____ = 5

35. ____ of 44 = 11 36. $\frac{1}{4} \times$ ____ = 10 37. $\frac{1}{6}$ of ____ = 2 38. $\frac{4}{7} \times 7 =$ ____

39. $\frac{1}{7}$ of ____ = 8 40. ____ $\times 8 = 2$ 41. $\frac{1}{8}$ of ____ = 8 42. $\frac{2}{9}$ of 72 = ____

43. ____ $\times 27 = 3$ 44. $\frac{3}{5} \times 15 =$ ____ 45. ____ of 81 = 9 46. $\frac{1}{3} \times$ ____ = 10

Solve.

47. Val surveyed 24 students and found that $\frac{7}{8}$ of them take the bus to school each day. How many students take the bus? ______________

48. Val surveyed 45 students and found that $\frac{3}{5}$ of them have pets. How many students have pets? ______________

Name: ____________

MULTIPLY FRACTIONS

Multiply using any method. Write the answer in simplest form.

1. $\frac{1}{4} \times \frac{2}{4} =$ ______
2. $\frac{1}{3} \times \frac{3}{5} =$ ______
3. $\frac{1}{2} \times \frac{2}{8} =$ ______
4. $\frac{1}{5} \times \frac{2}{3} =$ ______
5. $\frac{1}{2} \times \frac{3}{6} =$ ______
6. $\frac{1}{5} \times \frac{2}{4} =$ ______
7. $\frac{1}{4} \times \frac{6}{10} =$ ______
8. $\frac{1}{3} \times \frac{9}{10} =$ ______
9. $\frac{1}{3} \times \frac{5}{6} =$ ______
10. $\frac{1}{2} \times \frac{6}{10} =$ ______
11. $\frac{3}{6} \times \frac{1}{5} =$ ______
12. $\frac{2}{5} \times \frac{1}{4} =$ ______
13. $\frac{1}{5} \times \frac{5}{8} =$ ______
14. $\frac{4}{5} \times \frac{1}{4} =$ ______
15. $\frac{1}{3} \times \frac{3}{10} =$ ______
16. $\frac{1}{2} \times \frac{2}{3} =$ ______
17. $\frac{2}{5} \times \frac{7}{12} =$ ______
18. $\frac{5}{6} \times \frac{2}{3} =$ ______
19. $\frac{3}{4} \times \frac{3}{4} =$ ______
20. $\frac{2}{5} \times \frac{1}{8} =$ ______
21. $\frac{3}{4} \times \frac{1}{4} =$ ______
22. $\frac{4}{5} \times \frac{7}{10} =$ ______
23. $\frac{3}{5} \times \frac{5}{12} =$ ______
24. $\frac{4}{5} \times \frac{3}{4} =$ ______
25. $\frac{3}{5} \times \frac{11}{12} =$ ______
26. $\frac{3}{4} \times \frac{2}{5} =$ ______
27. $\frac{2}{3} \times \frac{3}{5} =$ ______
28. $\frac{4}{5} \times \frac{1}{2} =$ ______
29. $\frac{7}{8} \times \frac{3}{5} =$ ______
30. $\frac{3}{5} \times \frac{5}{6} =$ ______
31. $\frac{9}{10} \times \frac{2}{5} =$ ______
32. $\frac{1}{4} \times \frac{5}{6} =$ ______
33. $\frac{2}{5} \times \frac{3}{8} =$ ______
34. $\frac{5}{8} \times \frac{2}{3} =$ ______
35. $\frac{3}{4} \times \frac{5}{6} =$ ______
36. $\frac{9}{10} \times \frac{5}{6} =$ ______

Solve.

37. On Saturday, $\frac{3}{5}$ of the visitors to the public library were adults, and $\frac{2}{3}$ of the adults were female. What fraction of the visitors to the library on Saturday were adult females?

______

38. Fiction books make up $\frac{3}{8}$ of all the books in the library. Of these fiction books, $\frac{1}{3}$ are mystery or suspense novels. What fraction of books in the library are mystery or suspense?

______

Name: ____

MULTIPLY BY FRACTIONS

Multiply. Write the product in simplest form. Do as many as you can mentally.

1. $\frac{1}{2} \times \frac{1}{6} =$ ____
2. $\frac{2}{3} \times \frac{1}{3} =$ ____
3. $\frac{5}{6} \times 6 =$ ____
4. $\frac{3}{5} \times \frac{2}{3} =$ ____
5. $\frac{1}{3} \times \frac{3}{10} =$ ____
6. $\frac{1}{4} \times 8 =$ ____
7. $\frac{3}{10} \times \frac{2}{5} =$ ____
8. $\frac{1}{3} \times 12 =$ ____
9. $\frac{1}{4} \times \frac{4}{15} =$ ____
10. $\frac{3}{4} \times \frac{4}{9} =$ ____
11. $\frac{2}{3} \times \frac{9}{16} =$ ____
12. $\frac{1}{8} \times \frac{4}{5} =$ ____
13. $\frac{3}{4} \times \frac{3}{4} =$ ____
14. $\frac{5}{9} \times \frac{9}{10} =$ ____
15. $16 \times \frac{5}{8} =$ ____
16. $\frac{7}{8} \times \frac{4}{5} =$ ____
17. $\frac{7}{12} \times 12 =$ ____
18. $\frac{5}{12} \times \frac{5}{6} =$ ____
19. $\frac{3}{8} \times \frac{5}{24} =$ ____
20. $\frac{1}{10} \times \frac{20}{21} =$ ____
21. $\frac{7}{10} \times \frac{5}{7} =$ ____

Algebra Evaluate the expression.

22. $\frac{2}{3}x$ for $x = \frac{3}{4}$ ____
23. $\frac{1}{8}z$ for $z = \frac{2}{5}$ ____
24. $10u$ for $u = \frac{1}{2}$ ____
25. $\frac{7}{24}e$ for $e = 24$ ____
26. $28r$ for $r = \frac{2}{7}$ ____
27. $\frac{3}{8}n$ for $n = 16$ ____
28. $\frac{9}{10}x$ for $x = \frac{4}{5}$ ____
29. $\frac{1}{4}t$ for $t = \frac{9}{16}$ ____
30. $\frac{5}{8}u$ for $u = \frac{6}{7}$ ____

Solve.

31. Roberta turned $\frac{1}{8}$ of her backyard into a garden. She planted vegetables in $\frac{3}{4}$ of the garden. What fraction of Roberta's backyard has vegetables growing in it?

____

32. Tom plants alfalfa in his $\frac{1}{2}$-acre yard. If he uses $\frac{1}{3}$ of his yard for alfalfa, what fraction of an acre does the alfalfa occupy?

____

Name: ____________________

Mental Math: Estimate Products

Estimate the product.

1. $\frac{1}{7} \times 13$ ________
2. $11 \times \frac{4}{5}$ ________
3. $\frac{3}{16} \times 45$ ________
4. $\frac{2}{3} \times 19$ ________
5. $38 \times \frac{3}{8}$ ________
6. $\frac{1}{3} \times 23$ ________
7. $29 \times \frac{3}{4}$ ________
8. $\frac{1}{6} \times 31$ ________
9. $24\frac{1}{3} \times \frac{1}{5}$ ________
10. $\frac{3}{8} \times 25\frac{2}{7}$ ________
11. $\frac{2}{9} \times 46\frac{3}{4}$ ________
12. $34\frac{7}{8} \times \frac{1}{4}$ ________
13. $\frac{3}{10} \times 52\frac{1}{2}$ ________
14. $77\frac{3}{8} \times \frac{1}{16}$ ________
15. $\frac{3}{4} \times 51\frac{2}{7}$ ________
16. $\frac{3}{5} \times 61\frac{4}{5}$ ________
17. $63\frac{1}{6} \times \frac{1}{8}$ ________
18. $\frac{3}{7} \times 58$ ________

Tell whether the estimate is reasonable. Write *yes* or *no*.

19. $\frac{3}{8} \times 25$; 9 ________
20. $16\frac{1}{4} \times \frac{1}{2}$; 8 ________
21. $11\frac{3}{4} \times \frac{2}{3}$; 12 ________
22. $\frac{1}{8} \times 22$; 3 ________
23. $31\frac{1}{7} \times \frac{1}{3}$; 20 ________
24. $\frac{3}{4} \times 29$; 7 ________
25. $\frac{5}{8} \times 32$; 20 ________
26. $35\frac{1}{2} \times \frac{1}{4}$; 18 ________
27. $\frac{2}{5} \times 46$; 18 ________

Solve.

28. Fran wants to carpet $\frac{1}{3}$ of her studio. The total area of her studio is 1,482 square feet. About how many square feet will she carpet?

____

29. It took 25 hours to paint a home. If $\frac{3}{8}$ of the time was spent painting trim, about how many hours were spent painting trim?

____

Name: ____

MULTIPLY MIXED NUMBERS

Multiply. Write the answer in simplest form. Estimate to check the reasonableness of your answer.

1. $2 \times 1\frac{1}{2} =$ ____

2. $1\frac{1}{5} \times 5 =$ ____

3. $9 \times 4\frac{2}{3} =$ ____

4. $3\frac{1}{8} \times 4 =$ ____

5. $3\frac{4}{9} \times 3 =$ ____

6. $6 \times 3\frac{1}{2} =$ ____

7. $5\frac{2}{7} \times 7 =$ ____

8. $9 \times 6\frac{2}{3} =$ ____

9. $10 \times 1\frac{5}{6} =$ ____

10. $7\frac{5}{6} \times \frac{3}{4} =$ ____

11. $\frac{2}{5} \times 4\frac{3}{10} =$ ____

12. $7\frac{1}{9} \times \frac{3}{8} =$ ____

13. $5\frac{1}{4} \times \frac{1}{6} =$ ____

14. $\frac{3}{4} \times 3\frac{1}{6} =$ ____

15. $12\frac{1}{2} \times \frac{2}{5} =$ ____

16. $\frac{7}{8} \times 1\frac{3}{5} =$ ____

17. $2\frac{3}{4} \times 3\frac{1}{4} =$ ____

18. $1\frac{1}{2} \times 2\frac{1}{2} =$ ____

19. $4\frac{1}{5} \times 5\frac{2}{3} =$ ____

20. $6\frac{1}{4} \times 7\frac{1}{2} =$ ____

21. $1\frac{1}{2} \times \frac{3}{4} =$ ____

22. $2\frac{1}{5} \times 3 \times 2\frac{1}{4} =$ ____

23. $4 \times 1\frac{1}{5} \times \frac{1}{2} =$ ____

24. $2 \times 3\frac{3}{4} \times 1\frac{1}{10} =$ ____

25. $4\frac{1}{4} \times 2\frac{1}{8} \times 2 =$ ____

Algebra Evaluate the expression.

26. $6\frac{1}{2}a$ for $a = 14$ ____

27. $13n$ for $n = 1\frac{1}{3}$ ____

28. $\frac{3}{4}x$ for $x = 2\frac{1}{2}$ ____

29. $3\frac{1}{8}e$ for $e = \frac{8}{25}$ ____

Solve.

30. Seven and a half bricks are needed to brick an area of one square foot. How many bricks are needed for a wall of 80 square feet?

____

31. A mason is able to set $2\frac{1}{2}$ bricks in one minute. At that rate, how many bricks is the mason able to set in one hour?

____

Name: ______________________

Problem-Solving Strategy: Work Backward

✔ Read
✔ Plan
✔ Solve
✔ Look Back

Solve. Use the work-backward strategy.

1. Douglas is twice as old as Michelle. If the sum of their ages is 39, how old are they?

____

____

2. Dennis's age is half of Carolyn's age. If the sum of their ages is 45, how old are Carolyn and Dennis?

____

____

3. Mario is $\frac{1}{2}$ the age of Francis. Francis is 8 years younger than Jean. Jean is twice as old as Peter. Peter is 9. How old is Mario?

____

____

4. Tim is $\frac{1}{3}$ the age of Ben. Ben is 6 years older than Tim. How old is Ben?

____

____

Solve using any method.

5. When Patrick was born, his family celebrated by planting a 1-foot tall pine tree in their backyard. If Patrick is now 8 years old, and the tree grows about $1\frac{1}{2}$ feet each year, how tall is the tree?

____

6. Tom plants tomatoes. If the tomatoes grow for $\frac{1}{6}$ of the year each year, how many months out of 4 years do they grow?

____

7. On her sixteenth birthday, Oli's savings account had a balance of $620. If she adds $15 each month to her account, what will her account balance be on her eighteenth birthday?

____

8. **Write a problem** that describes the ages of various people and asks a question about age. Solve your own problem and then ask a classmate to solve it.

____

Name: ____________

Divide Fractions

Divide using any method. Write the answer in simplest form.

1. $2 \div \frac{1}{2} =$ ______
2. $1 \div \frac{1}{3} =$ ______
3. $3 \div \frac{1}{5} =$ ______
4. $2 \div \frac{1}{10} =$ ______
5. $\frac{5}{8} \div \frac{1}{8} =$ ______
6. $\frac{3}{5} \div \frac{1}{5} =$ ______
7. $\frac{1}{6} \div \frac{1}{12} =$ ______
8. $\frac{1}{3} \div \frac{1}{6} =$ ______
9. $\frac{4}{5} \div \frac{2}{5} =$ ______
10. $4 \div \frac{1}{4} =$ ______
11. $\frac{7}{8} \div \frac{1}{8} =$ ______
12. $\frac{3}{4} \div \frac{3}{8} =$ ______
13. $2 \div \frac{1}{8} =$ ______
14. $\frac{1}{2} \div \frac{1}{6} =$ ______
15. $1 \div \frac{1}{4} =$ ______
16. $\frac{2}{3} \div \frac{1}{12} =$ ______
17. $\frac{2}{3} \div \frac{1}{6} =$ ______
18. $1 \div \frac{1}{5} =$ ______
19. $\frac{3}{4} \div \frac{1}{8} =$ ______
20. $2 \div \frac{1}{4} =$ ______
21. $3 \div \frac{1}{6} =$ ______
22. $\frac{2}{3} \div \frac{1}{6} =$ ______
23. $6 \div \frac{3}{4} =$ ______
24. $\frac{4}{5} \div \frac{1}{10} =$ ______
25. $\frac{3}{5} \div \frac{1}{5} =$ ______
26. $\frac{2}{3} \div \frac{2}{6} =$ ______
27. $5 \div \frac{5}{7} =$ ______
28. $12 \div \frac{2}{3} =$ ______
29. $\frac{3}{4} \div \frac{1}{4} =$ ______
30. $\frac{1}{2} \div \frac{1}{10} =$ ______

Compare. Write $>$, $<$, or $=$.

31. $2 \div \frac{1}{2}$ ◯ 2×2
32. $\frac{1}{3} \div \frac{1}{3}$ ◯ $\frac{1}{2} \div \frac{1}{6}$
33. 3×1 ◯ $\frac{3}{4} \div \frac{1}{4}$
34. $\frac{4}{5} \div \frac{1}{5}$ ◯ $\frac{1}{5} \div \frac{1}{10}$
35. $2 \div \frac{1}{6}$ ◯ $3 \div \frac{1}{3}$
36. $\frac{1}{2} \div \frac{1}{4}$ ◯ $1 \div \frac{1}{3}$
37. $\frac{1}{5} \div \frac{1}{5}$ ◯ $\frac{1}{5} \div 5$
38. $3 \div \frac{1}{6}$ ◯ $6 \div \frac{1}{4}$
39. $4 \div \frac{1}{4}$ ◯ $32 \div 2$
40. $2\frac{1}{4}$ ◯ $\frac{1}{3} \div 6$
41. $4 \times \frac{1}{4}$ ◯ $5 \div \frac{1}{5}$
42. $6 \div \frac{1}{3}$ ◯ $9 \div \frac{1}{2}$
43. $2 \times \frac{1}{3}$ ◯ $\frac{2}{3} \div \frac{1}{3}$
44. $\frac{1}{6} \div \frac{1}{3}$ ◯ $4 \div \frac{1}{2}$
45. $5 \div \frac{1}{5}$ ◯ $3 \div \frac{1}{8}$
46. $\frac{3}{4} \div \frac{3}{4}$ ◯ $\frac{1}{3} \times 3$
47. $\frac{2}{5} \times 10$ ◯ $\frac{2}{3} \div \frac{1}{6}$
48. $12 \times \frac{1}{4}$ ◯ $2 \div \frac{2}{5}$
49. $\frac{7}{8} \div \frac{1}{8}$ ◯ $\frac{56}{8} \times \frac{8}{8}$
50. $\frac{3}{7} \div \frac{7}{2}$ ◯ $\frac{1}{3} \times \frac{1}{2}$
51. $9 \div \frac{2}{3}$ ◯ $27 \times \frac{1}{2}$
52. $5 \div \frac{1}{6}$ ◯ $65 \times \frac{1}{3}$
53. $16 \div \frac{7}{8}$ ◯ $42 \times \frac{1}{2}$
54. $15 \div \frac{3}{4}$ ◯ $45 \times \frac{2}{3}$
55. $26 \div \frac{3}{5}$ ◯ $85 \times \frac{1}{2}$
56. $\frac{3}{4} \div \frac{9}{10}$ ◯ $93 \times \frac{1}{3}$
57. $5 \div \frac{3}{5}$ ◯ $64 \times \frac{1}{8}$

Name: ____________________

DIVIDE WITH FRACTIONS

Divide. Write your answer in simplest form.

1. $\frac{1}{2} \div \frac{3}{5} =$ ______
2. $\frac{1}{3} \div \frac{1}{4} =$ ______
3. $\frac{3}{4} \div 3 =$ ______
4. $\frac{2}{3} \div 8 =$ ______
5. $\frac{1}{4} \div \frac{1}{3} =$ ______
6. $\frac{1}{5} \div 5 =$ ______
7. $\frac{1}{4} \div 10 =$ ______
8. $\frac{1}{2} \div \frac{3}{8} =$ ______
9. $\frac{2}{3} \div \frac{1}{3} =$ ______
10. $\frac{3}{4} \div \frac{1}{6} =$ ______
11. $\frac{1}{3} \div \frac{5}{6} =$ ______
12. $\frac{2}{3} \div \frac{2}{5} =$ ______
13. $\frac{3}{5} \div \frac{4}{5} =$ ______
14. $\frac{2}{3} \div 18 =$ ______
15. $\frac{1}{2} \div \frac{4}{5} =$ ______
16. $\frac{1}{4} \div \frac{5}{8} =$ ______
17. $12 \div \frac{1}{2} =$ ______
18. $\frac{1}{4} \div \frac{2}{5} =$ ______
19. $\frac{3}{4} \div \frac{3}{8} =$ ______
20. $\frac{1}{5} \div \frac{2}{5} =$ ______
21. $\frac{4}{9} \div 8 =$ ______
22. $\frac{5}{8} \div \frac{3}{4} =$ ______
23. $8 \div \frac{1}{4} =$ ______
24. $18 \div \frac{1}{3} =$ ______
25. $\frac{1}{3} \div \frac{5}{9} =$ ______
26. $\frac{3}{4} \div 8 =$ ______
27. $\frac{3}{10} \div 9 =$ ______
28. $\frac{2}{3} \div \frac{7}{9} =$ ______
29. $\frac{5}{8} \div 5 =$ ______
30. $\frac{7}{10} \div \frac{3}{4} =$ ______
31. $\frac{2}{3} \div 21 =$ ______
32. $\frac{5}{12} \div 10 =$ ______

Algebra Simplify using the order-of-operation rules.

33. $(\frac{1}{3} \div \frac{3}{5}) + \frac{1}{9}$ ______
34. $\frac{2}{3} + (\frac{1}{3} \div \frac{1}{3})$ ______
35. $\frac{1}{4} \times \frac{3}{8} + \frac{1}{16}$ ______
36. $\frac{5}{8} - \frac{1}{4} \div 2$ ______
37. $\frac{4}{5} \times 5 + \frac{1}{2}$ ______
38. $\frac{3}{4} \div (\frac{1}{4} \times 2) + \frac{3}{4}$ ______

Solve.

39. Nails are made from wire. Suppose it takes $\frac{7}{8}$ inch of wire to make a nail. How many whole nails can be made from a wire that is 12 inches long?

____

40. Jim uses $\frac{1}{2}$ of a container to hold nails. Each nail takes up $\frac{1}{16}$ of the container. How many nails are in the container?

____

Name: ______

Divide with Mixed Numbers

Divide. Write your answer in simplest form. Estimate to check the reasonableness of your answer.

1. $2\frac{1}{2} \div 1\frac{1}{4} =$ ______ **2.** $1\frac{1}{4} \div \frac{9}{10} =$ ______ **3.** $1\frac{3}{4} \div \frac{1}{2} =$ ______

4. $3 \div 4\frac{1}{5} =$ ______ **5.** $\frac{11}{12} \div 3\frac{2}{3} =$ ______ **6.** $4 \div 1\frac{1}{3} =$ ______

7. $2\frac{7}{8} \div \frac{5}{8} =$ ______ **8.** $3\frac{3}{8} \div \frac{7}{8} =$ ______ **9.** $5\frac{3}{4} \div \frac{3}{8} =$ ______

10. $3\frac{1}{8} \div 3 =$ ______ **11.** $\frac{3}{5} \div 1\frac{7}{10} =$ ______ **12.** $1\frac{3}{8} \div \frac{4}{9} =$ ______

13. $6 \div 2\frac{1}{3} =$ ______ **14.** $6\frac{5}{12} \div \frac{11}{12} =$ ______ **15.** $9 \div 3\frac{3}{8} =$ ______

16. $2\frac{3}{4} \div 1\frac{1}{2} =$ ______ **17.** $1\frac{3}{10} \div 2\frac{3}{5} =$ ______ **18.** $\frac{5}{6} \div 1\frac{2}{3} =$ ______

19. $3\frac{3}{4} \div 2\frac{1}{2} =$ ______ **20.** $2\frac{5}{8} \div 1\frac{3}{4} =$ ______ **21.** $1\frac{3}{4} \div 3\frac{7}{8} =$ ______

Algebra Ring the letter of the missing number.

22. $\square \div 3 = \frac{1}{2}$ **a.** 3 **b.** $\frac{5}{2}$ **c.** 2 **d.** $\frac{3}{2}$

23. $3\frac{3}{4} \div \square = 3$ **a.** $1\frac{1}{4}$ **b.** $1\frac{3}{8}$ **c.** $1\frac{1}{2}$ **d.** $1\frac{5}{8}$

24. $1\frac{1}{2} \div \square = 3\frac{3}{4}$ **a.** $\frac{2}{3}$ **b.** $\frac{2}{5}$ **c.** $\frac{3}{2}$ **d.** $\frac{5}{2}$

25. $\square \div 2 = \frac{9}{16}$ **a.** $\frac{9}{32}$ **b.** $\frac{9}{16}$ **c.** $\frac{9}{8}$ **d.** $\frac{9}{4}$

Solve.

26. A charity wants to distribute $4\frac{1}{2}$ cases of fruit. If each of 10 families is to receive the same quantity, how much will each family receive?

______

27. A charity wants to distribute $10\frac{1}{2}$ gallons of milk. If the charity gives $\frac{3}{4}$ gallon of milk to each family, how many families will receive milk?

______

Name: ____________________

Customary Units of Length

Choose an appropriate unit for measuring the length. Write *in., ft, yd,* or *mi.*

1. length of a soccer field ________

2. width of your classroom ________

3. height of a tree ________

4. width of an ocean ________

5. length of a street ________

6. thickness of a wall ________

7. width of a door ________

8. length of your shoe ________

9. height of a building ________

10. width of a sandwich ________

11. length of a pen ________

12. height of a ceiling ________

Complete.

13. 8 ft = ________ in.

14. 2 yd = ________ ft

15. 48 in. = ________ ft

16. 3 mi = ________ ft

17. 8 ft = ________ yd

18. 1 ft 4 in. = ________ in.

19. 2 yd 1 ft = ________ ft

20. 18 in. = ____ ft ____ in.

21. 1 mi = ________ yd

22. 3 ft 4 in. = ________ in.

23. $7\frac{1}{3}$ yd = ________ ft

24. $2\frac{1}{2}$ ft = ________ in.

25. 78 in. = ________ ft

26. $\frac{3}{10}$ mi = ________ ft

27. 100 in. = ____ ft ____ in.

28. 6 yd = ________ in.

29. $2\frac{1}{2}$ mi = ________ in.

30. 81 ft = ________ yd

Solve.

31. How many feet deep is a body of water that is 23 yards deep?

____

32. How many miles is a race that is 7,040 yards long?

____

Name: ____________________

Customary Units of Capacity and Weight

Choose an appropriate unit for measuring.

1. capacity of a pail ________
2. weight of a locomotive ________
3. amount of water in a pool ________
4. weight of a desk ________
5. capacity of a water cooler ________
6. weight of a refrigerator ________
7. capacity of a small container ________
8. weight of a bookend ________
9. weight of a paperback book ________
10. weight of an envelope ________
11. weight of a plant and its pot ____
12. weight of your mathematics book ____

Complete.

13. 4 gal = ________ qt
14. 2 qt = ________ c
15. 3,000 lb = ______ T
16. 32 oz = ________ lb
17. 40 fl oz = ________ qt
18. 12 c = ________ qt
19. 1 gal = ________ pt
20. $4\frac{1}{2}$ T = ________ lb
21. $2\frac{1}{2}$ qt = ________ pt
22. 7,500 lb = ________ T
23. 88 oz = ________ lb
24. $6\frac{1}{2}$ gal = ________ qt
25. $5\frac{1}{4}$ qt = ________ c
26. 8 oz = ________ pint
27. 72 oz = ____ lb ____ oz
28. 4 c = ________ oz
29. $\frac{1}{4}$ gallon = ________ qt
30. 51 fl oz = ____ c ____ oz

Solve.

31. A pail contains $1\frac{1}{2}$ gallons of water. How many quarts of water does the pail hold?

____

32. A truck is loaded with 500 pounds of brick. How many tons of brick does the truck have?

____

Name:

Practice 75

Problem Solving: Choose Whether to Use Fractions or Decimals

✔ Read
✔ Plan
✔ Solve
✔ Look Back

Solve by choosing whether to use fractions or decimals.

1. A trucking company has a contract to deliver 15 yards of topsoil to a new home. How much of the task has been completed if 5 yards have already been delivered?

2. The 675-square-foot roof of a home is shingled. One bundle of shingles covers 20 square feet. How many bundles are used to shingle the roof?

3. A 2-by-4 wooden beam costs $5.25. How much do 3 beams cost?

4. A twenty-pound bag of soil costs $3. How much should an eight-pound bag cost?

Solve using any method.

5. A 17,250-square-foot lawn is seeded. If 1 pound of seed covers 400 square feet, how many pounds of seed are needed to seed the lawn?

6. Water from a well flows at a rate of 8 gallons per minute. At that rate, how long will it take to fill a holding tank that has a capacity of 35 gallons?

7. One cubic yard of concrete covers 81 square feet. How much concrete is needed for a driveway with an area of 1,620 square feet?

8. A board measures $92\frac{5}{8}$ inches in length. Estimate the total length of 2 of these boards in yards.

Name: ______________________

Classify 2-Dimensional Shapes

Write the name for each shaded figure.

1. 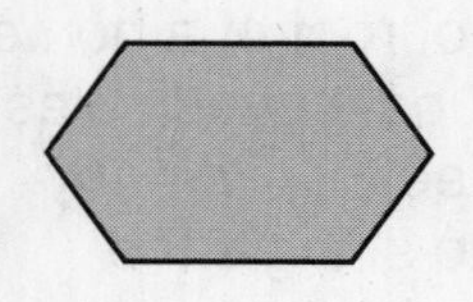

____

2. 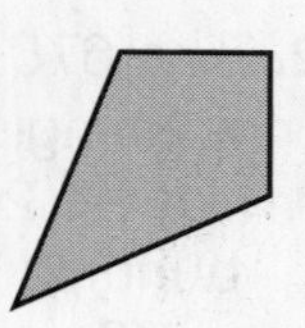

____

3. 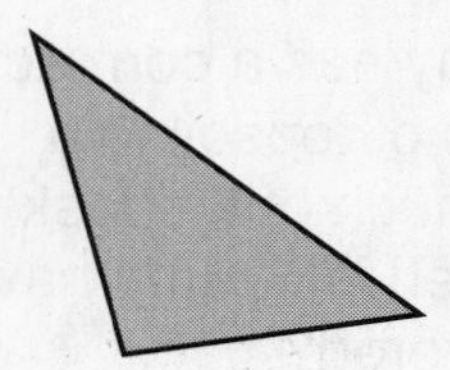

____

4. 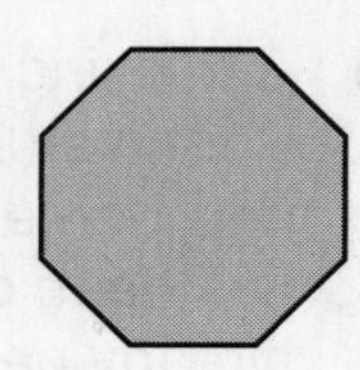

____

5. 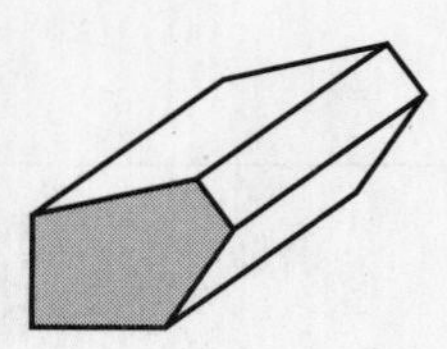

____

6. 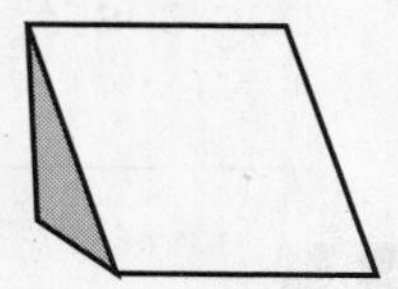

____

7. 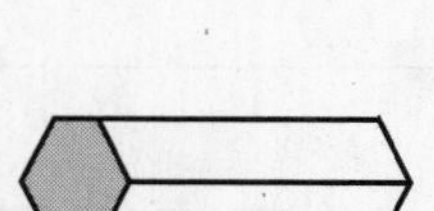

____

8. 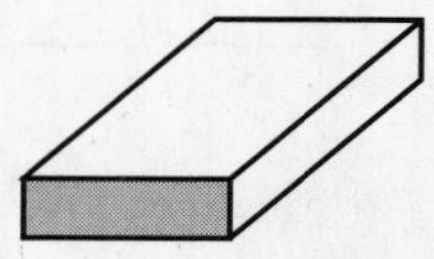

____

9. 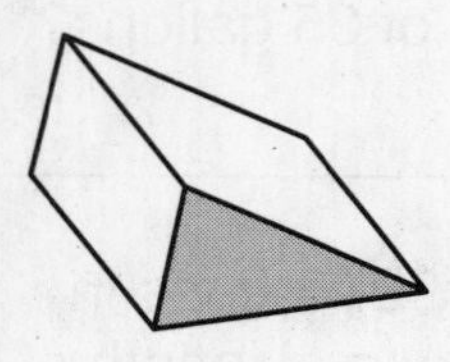

____

10. 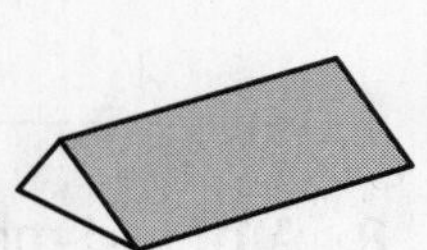

____

11. 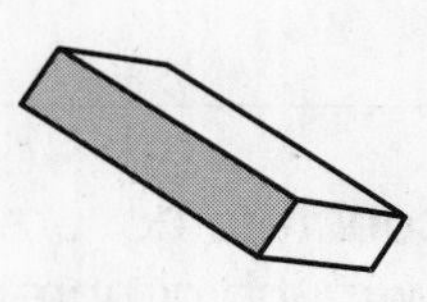

____

12. 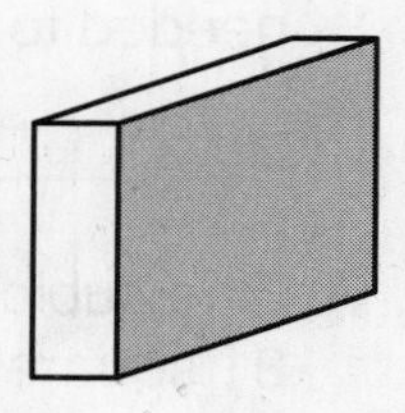

____

13. 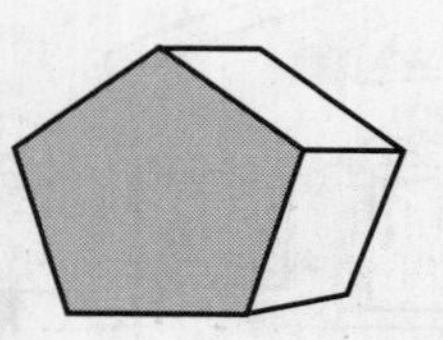

____

14. 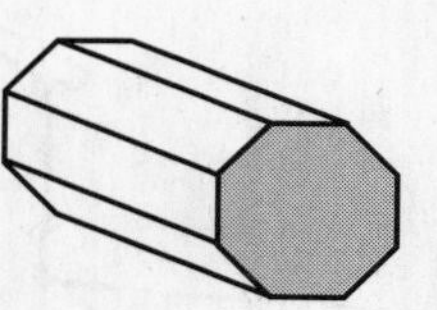

____

15. 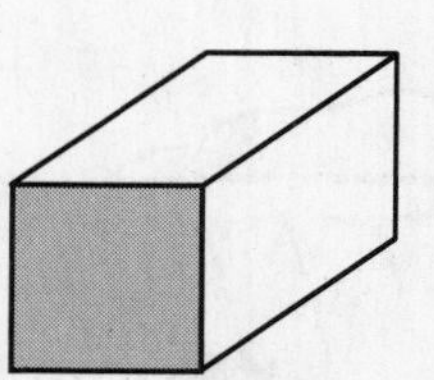

____

16. 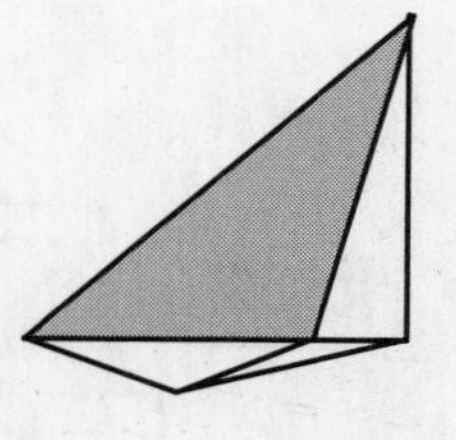

____

Name: ______________________________

Estimate and Measure Angles

Measure and classify each angle.

1. 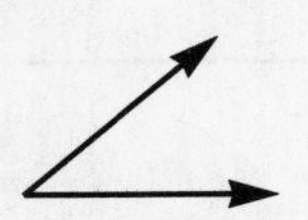

____

2. 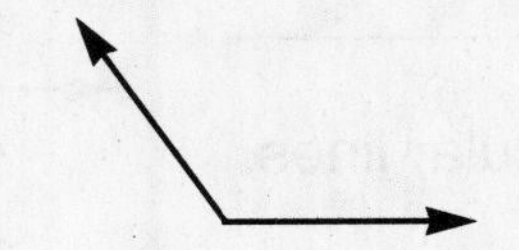

____

3. 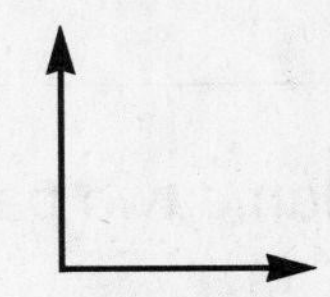

____

4. 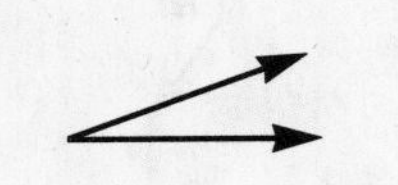

____

5. 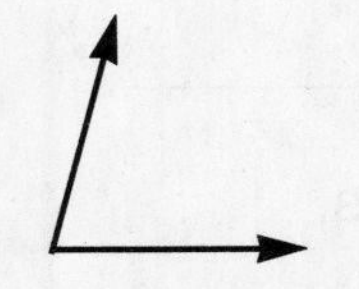

____

6. 

____

Estimate the measure of each angle and then measure it to check your estimate.

7. 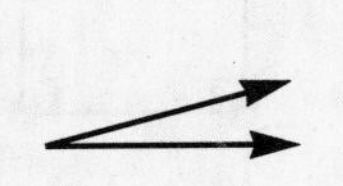

____

8. 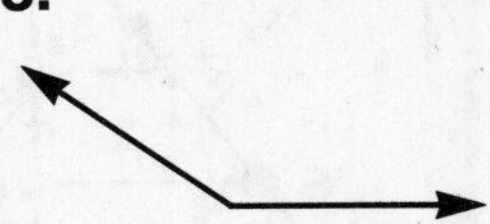

____

9. 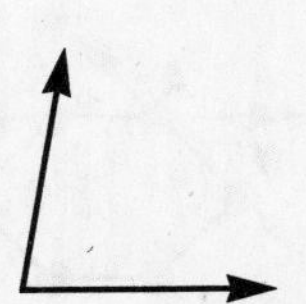

____

10. 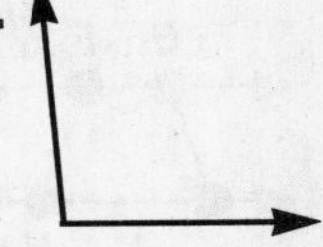

____

11. 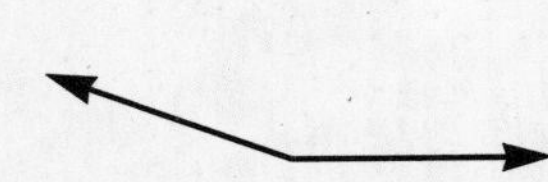

____

12. 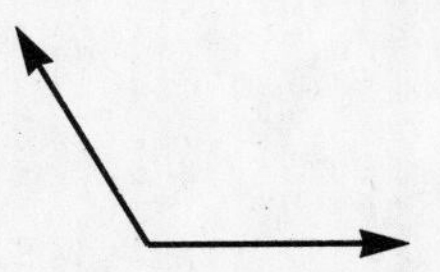

____

13. 

____

14. 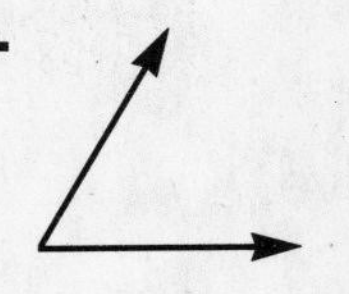

____

Find the measure of each angle in the triangle.

15. $\angle X$ ______________________

16. $\angle Y$ ______________________

17. $\angle Z$ ______________________

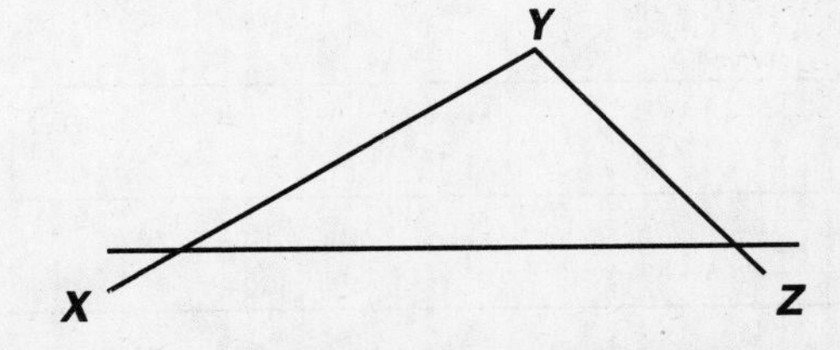

Name: ____________________

LINES

Use the diagram at the right for exercises 1–4.

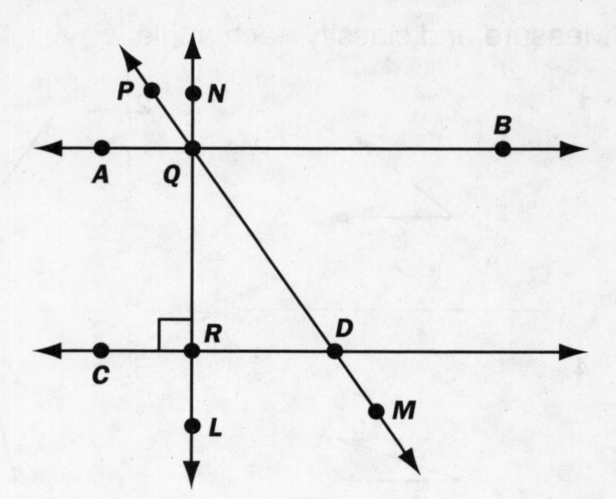

1. Name a pair of parallel lines.

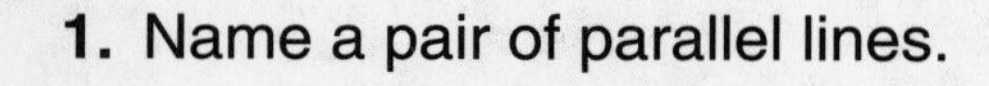

2. Name two pairs of perpendicular lines.

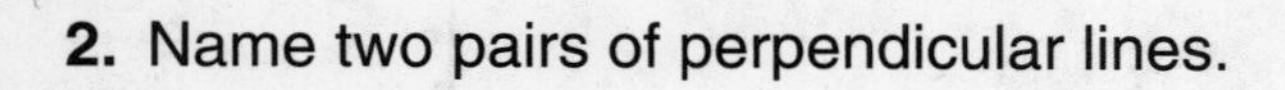

3. Name two pairs of intersecting lines.

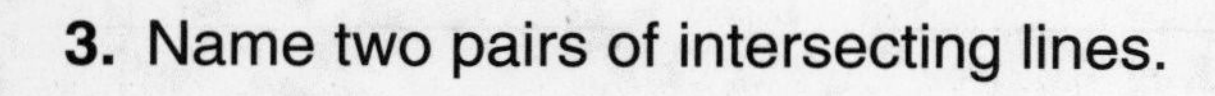

4. Name two pairs of equal angles.

____

____

Tell if the lines in the illustration are *intersecting, perpendicular,* or *parallel.*

5.

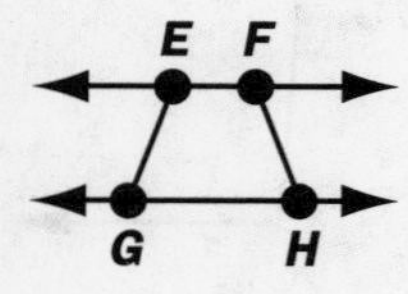

____

6.

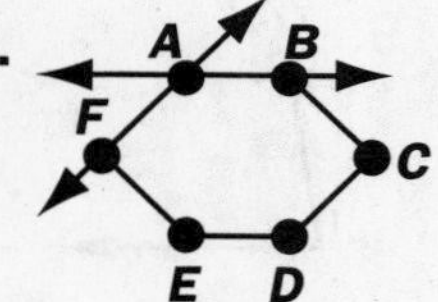

____

7.

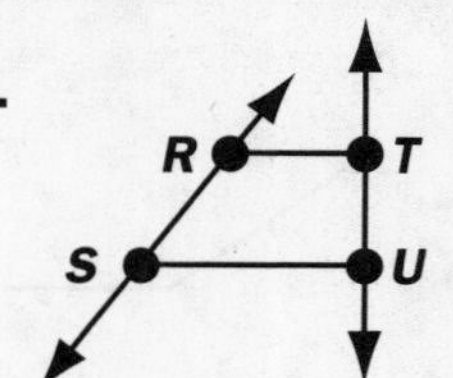

____

8.

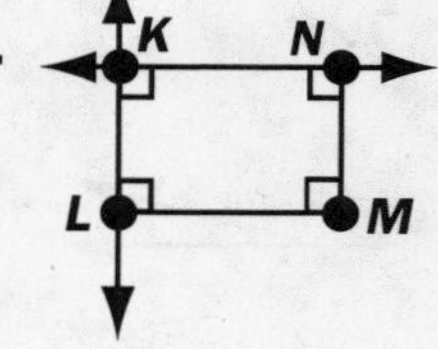

____

Solve.

9. Suppose the lines in the figure at the right represent railroad tracks. What type of lines do the tracks form?

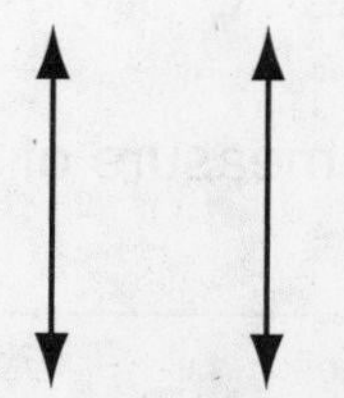

____

____

____

____

Name:

TRIANGLES AND QUADRILATERALS

Give all the possible ways to classify each polygon.

1.

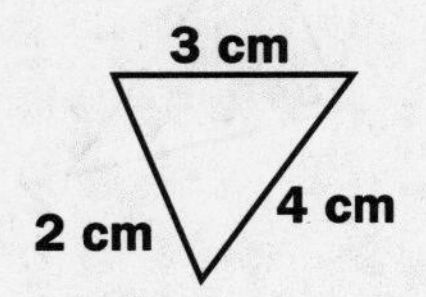

2.

2 cm
6 cm
6 cm
2 cm

3.

7 cm
4 cm
4 cm

4.

5 cm
7 cm
6 cm
4 cm

5.

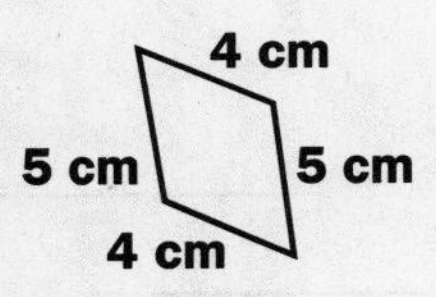

6.

3 cm
4 cm
5 cm

7.

3 cm
3 cm
3 cm
3 cm

8.

4 cm
4 cm
3 cm

Write *true* or *false.*

9. All the angles of a square and a rectangle have the same measure.

10. A trapezoid may have as many as three right angles.

11. Four triangles are created when the diagonals of a quadrilateral are drawn.

12. Opposite sides of a rhombus, a parallelogram, and a rectangle are congruent and parallel.

Name: ______________________________

Sums of Angles

Find the missing measure. Use what you know about quadrilaterals.

1. 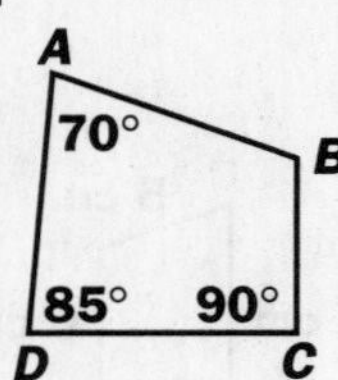

____

2. 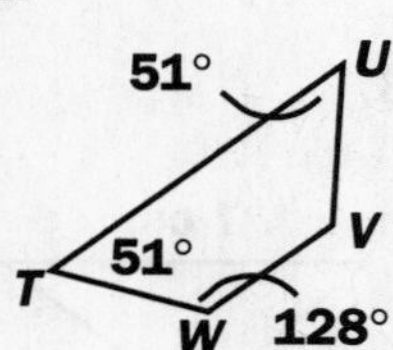

____

3. 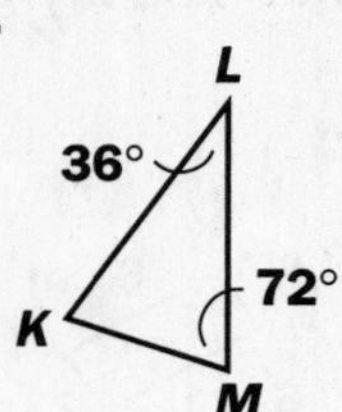

____

4. 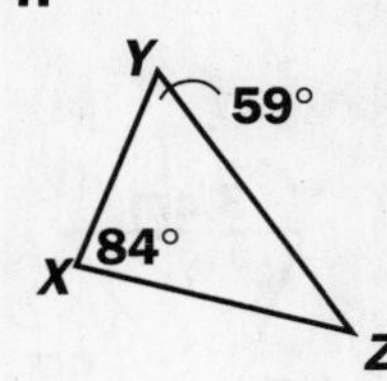

____

5. 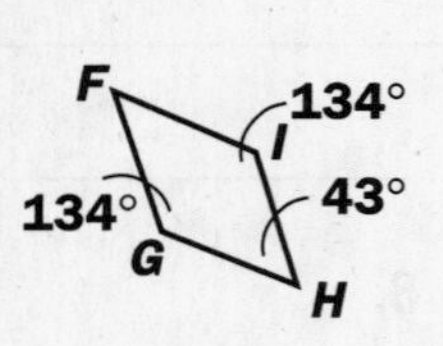

____

6. 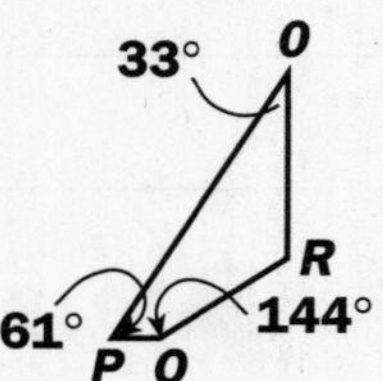

____

7. 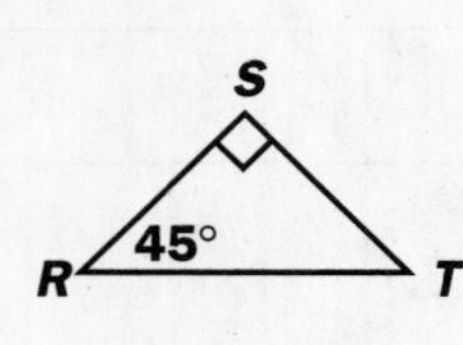

____

8. 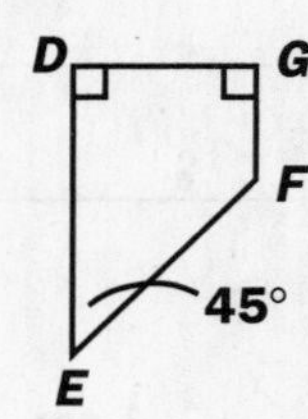

____

Solve.

9. The rectangle at the right was made from pattern blocks. What was the measure of $\angle X$, $\angle Y$, and $\angle Z$?

____

____

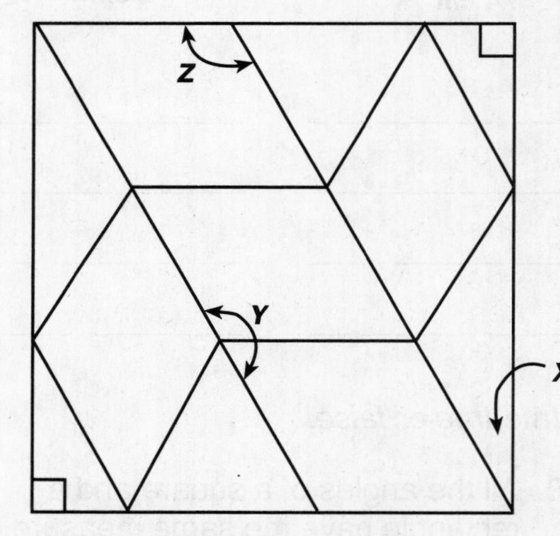

10. Can a quadrilateral have two angles that each measure 150°? Explain.

____

____

____

11. One of the angles of a rhombus is 120°. What are the other angles?

____

____

____

Name: ______

Problem-Solving Strategy: Make a Model

✔ Read
✔ Plan
✔ Solve
✔ Look Back

Solve using the make-a-model strategy.

1. Which group or groups of line segments will make a triangle? Sketch the triangle(s).

   a. 1 in., 2 in., 2 in.

   b. 1 in., 2 in., $3\frac{1}{2}$ in.

   c. $1\frac{1}{2}$ in., $2\frac{1}{2}$ in., $3\frac{1}{2}$ in.

   d. 2 in., 4 in., 7 in.

   ______

2. Which group or groups of segments below can be combined to form a quadrilateral? Sketch the quadrilateral(s).

   a. 1 in., 2 in., 3 in., 7 in.

   b. 1 in., $1\frac{1}{2}$ in., $2\frac{1}{2}$ in., 5 in.

   c. $\frac{1}{2}$ in., $1\frac{1}{2}$ in., $3\frac{1}{2}$ in., $6\frac{1}{2}$ in.

   d. 2 in., 3 in., 4 in., $5\frac{1}{2}$ in.

   ______

Solve using any method.

3. In the figures at the right, 3 points can be connected by 3 segments, 4 points can be connected by 6 segments, and 5 points can be connected by 10 segments. Continue the pattern to determine how many segments can be connected using 8 points.

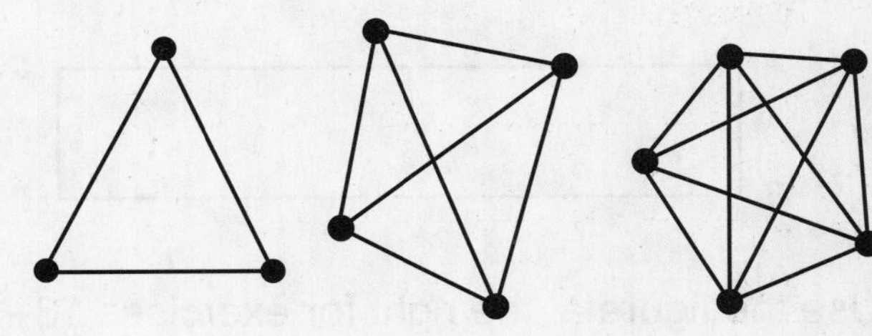

   ______

4. **Spatial Reasoning** How many different squares can be found in the figure at the right?

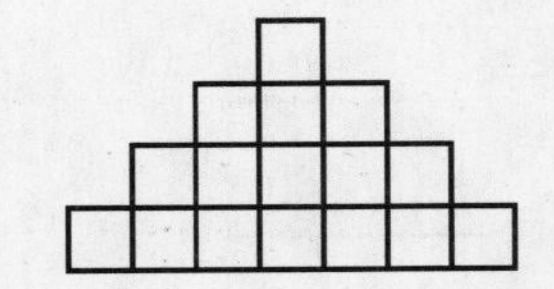

   ______

Name: ____________________

Constructions

Use a compass and straightedge to construct the congruent line segment or angle.

1. 

2. N ———— P

3. 

4. 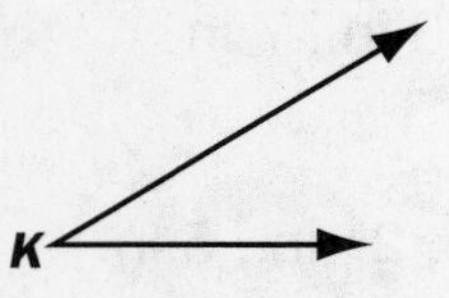

5. 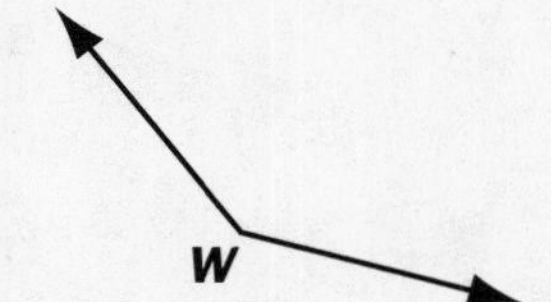

6. 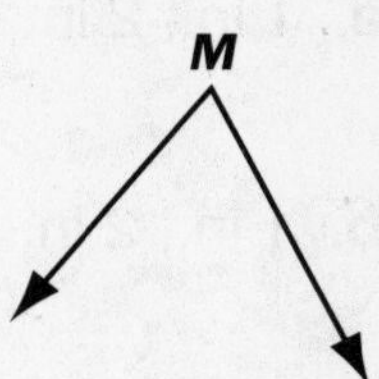

Use a compass and a straightedge to bisect the following.

7. a 72° angle

8. a 6.5-cm line segment

9. a $3\frac{3}{8}$-inch line segment

10. a 131° angle

11. *BD*

12. ∠*L*

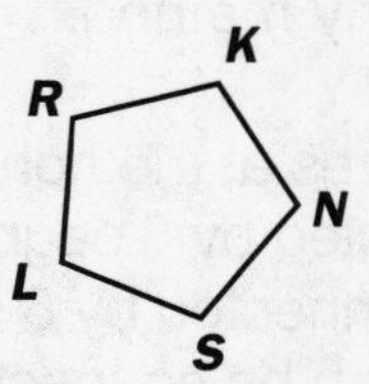

Use the figure at the right for exercises 13–17. Find the measure of each angle. *AE* is the bisector of ∠*DAB*.

13. ∠*ABC* = ________

14. ∠*DCB* = ________

15. ∠*BAE* = ________

16. ∠*DAE* = ________

17. ∠*ADC* = ________

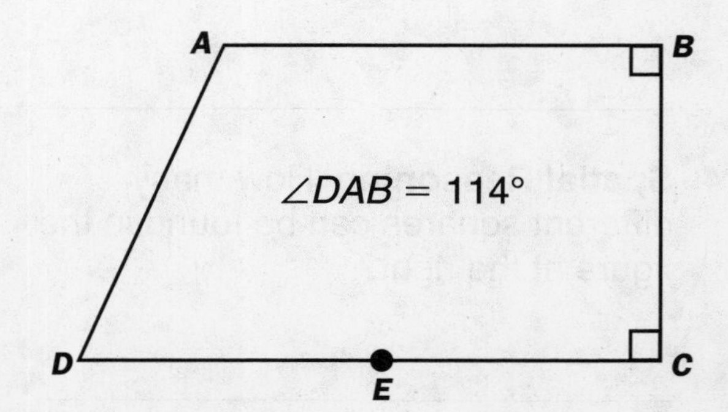

Name: ______________________________

Circles

Use the circle shown for exercises 1–7.

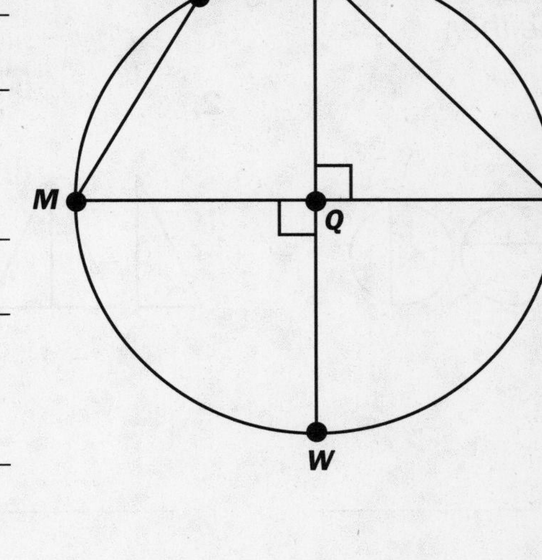

1. Name the chords. ____________________

2. Name the diameter(s). ____________________

3. Name the radii.

____

4. What is the measure of $\angle WQJ$? ____________________

5. What is the sum of the measures of $\angle MQC$, $\angle CQG$, and $\angle GQJ$? ____________________

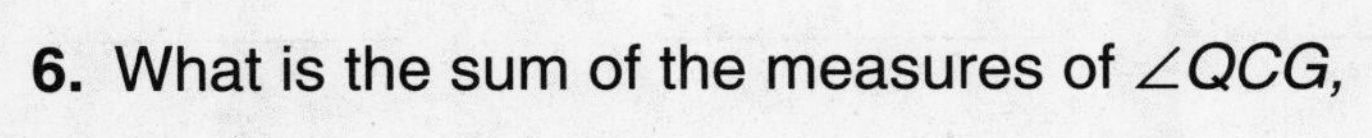

6. What is the sum of the measures of $\angle QCG$, $\angle QGC$, and $\angle CQG$? ____________________

7. What kind of triangle is ΔQJG? Explain.

____

____

Use the circle at the right for exercises 8–13. Write >, <, or =.

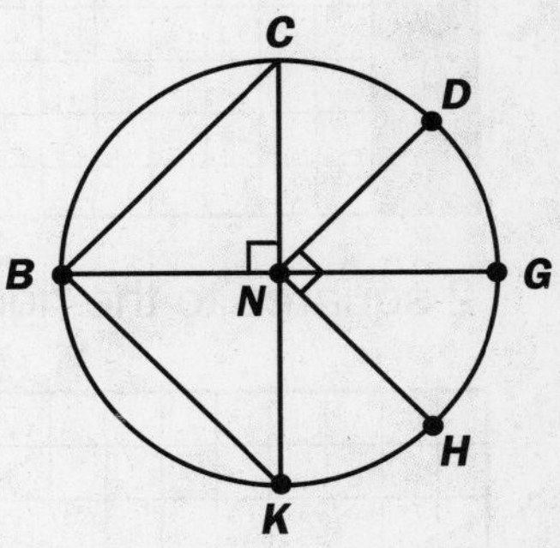

8. $\overline{KN}$ ◯ $\overline{NG}$

9. $\angle BNC$ ◯ $\angle CND$

10. $\angle KNH + \angle CND$ ◯ 180°

11. $\overline{GB}$ ◯ $\overline{CN}$

12. $\overline{BN}$ ◯ $\overline{CK}$

13. $\angle CBN + \angle NCB$ ◯ 90°

Use the diagram to solve.

14. In circle *R*, *RX* is a radius and *T* is the midpoint of *RX*. How does the length of *TX* compare with the length of *YX*?

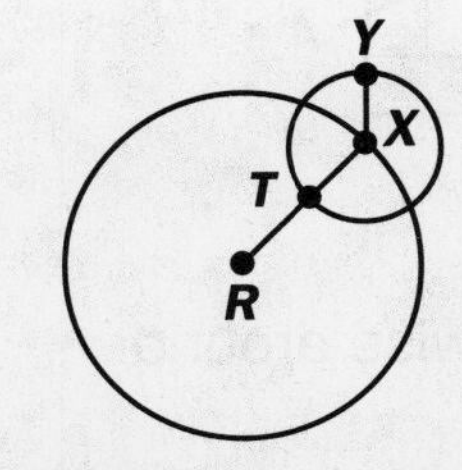

____

Name:

Practice 84

TRANSLATIONS AND ROTATIONS

Identify each pair of figures or the motions as a *translation*, *rotation*, or *neither*.

1.

2. 

3.

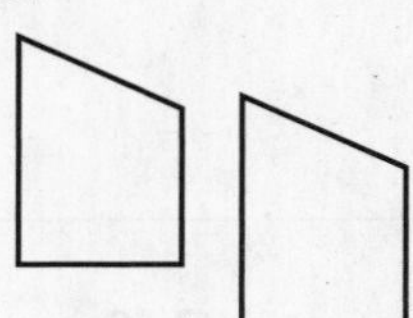

4.

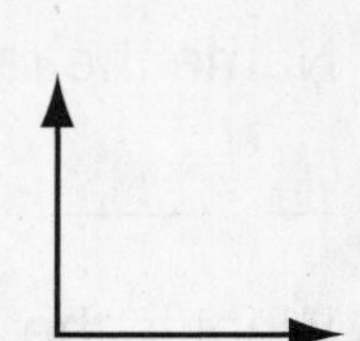

5. unscrewing the lid of a jar

6. blinking your eyelids

7. nodding yes or no

8. spinning a spinner

Draw the new figure after the described translation or rotation.

9.

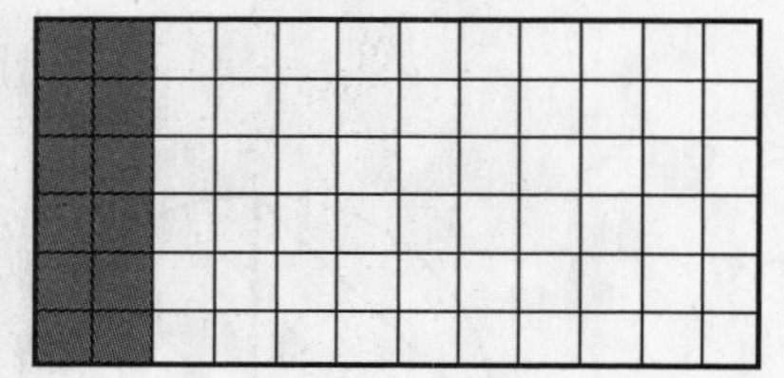

2 squares to the right

10.

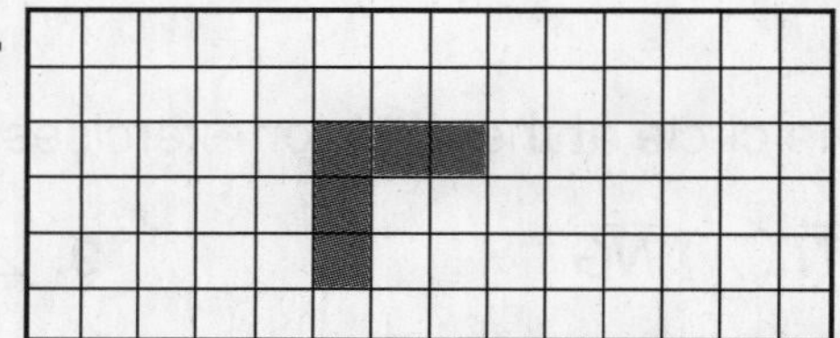

1 square up, then 2 squares left

11.

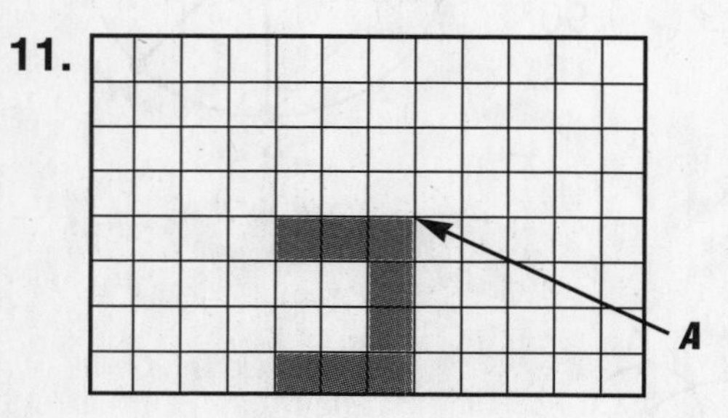

rotate 90° counterclockwise around point *A*

12.

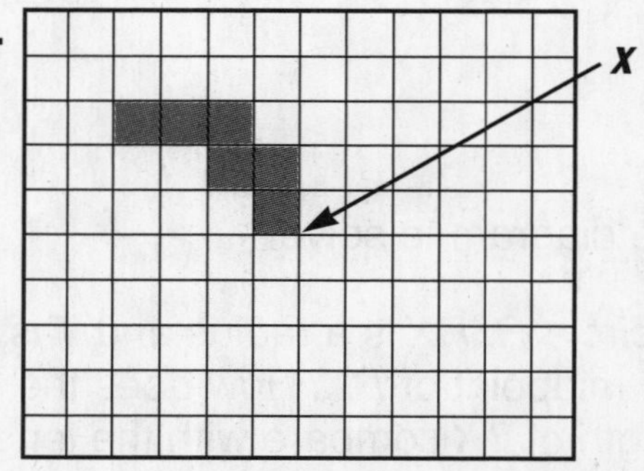

rotate 180° counterclockwise around point *X*

Name: ______________________

Reflections and Line Symmetry

Is the dashed line a line of symmetry? Write *yes* or *no*.

1.

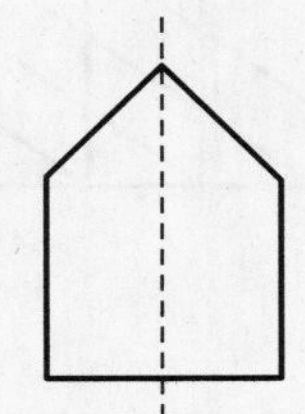

____

2.

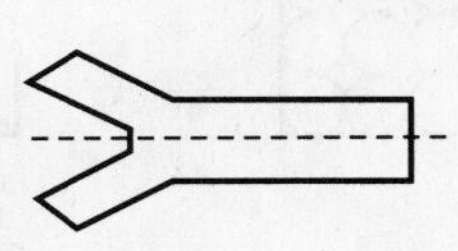

____

3.

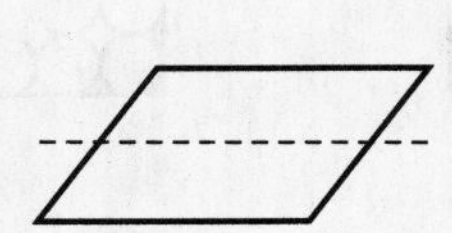

____

4.

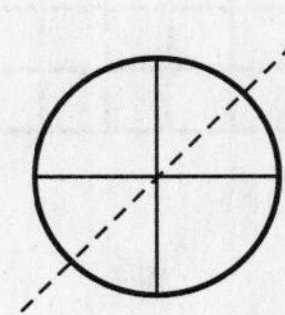

____

5.

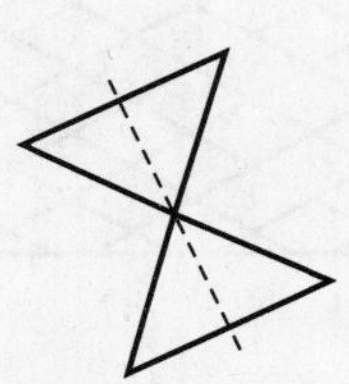

____

6.

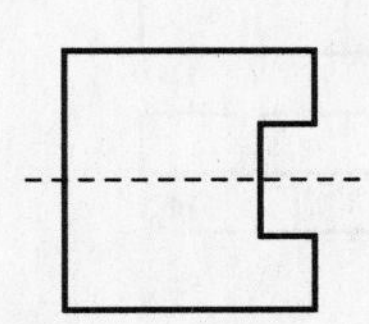

____

7.

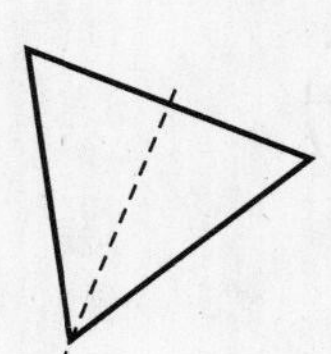

____

8.

____

Draw the reflection of the figure.

9.

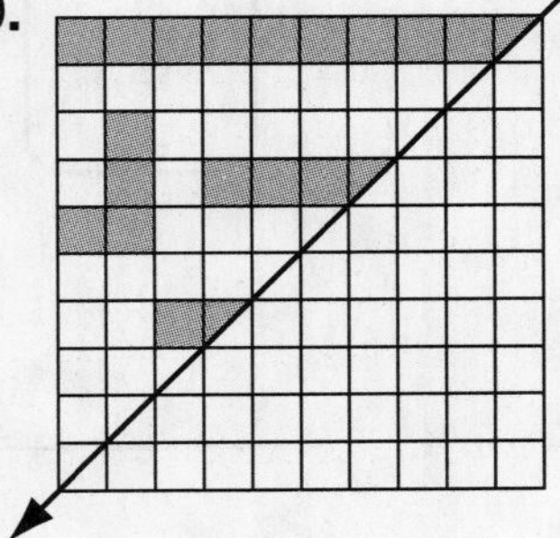

10.

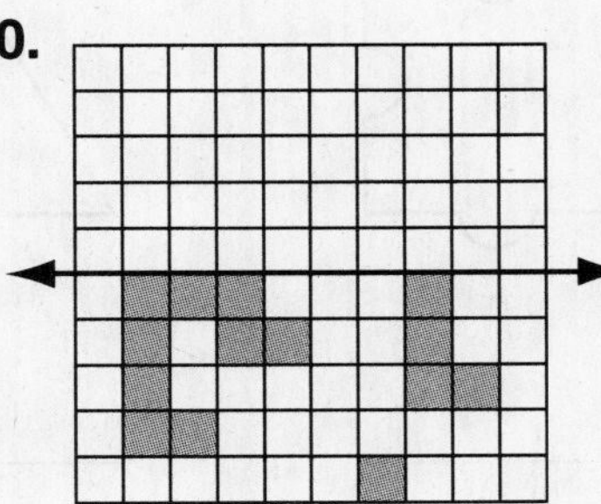

11.

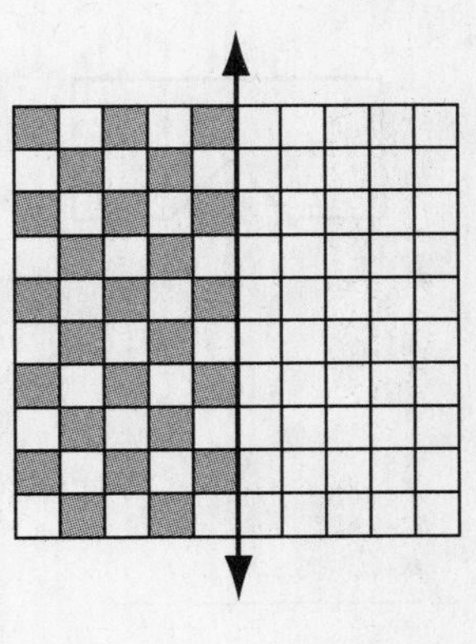

Solve.

12. What motion or motions might have occurred to the figure on the left for it to arrive in the position on the right?

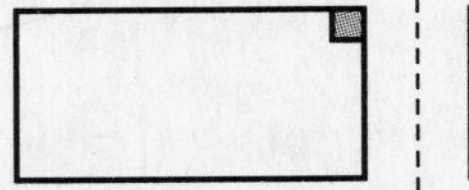

____

13. What motion or motions might have occurred to the figure on the left for it to arrive in the position on the right?

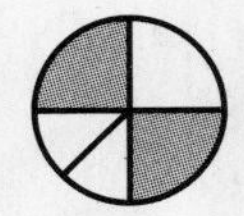

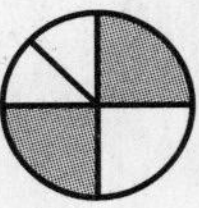

____

Name:

TESSELLATIONS

Tell whether each of the following is an example of a tessellation.

1. 

2. 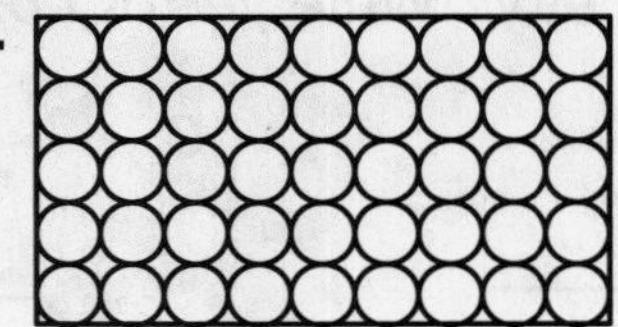

3. 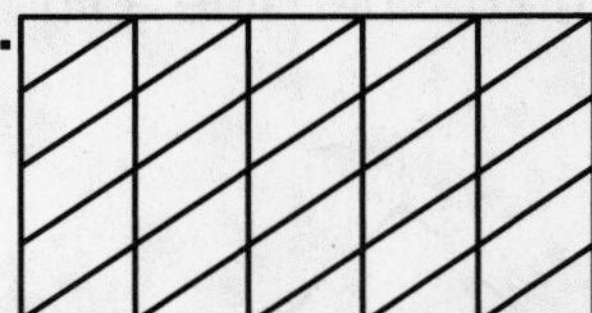

4. 

5. 

6. 

Identify the shapes that will tessellate. Tell why.

7. 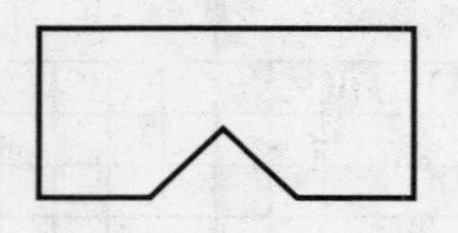

8. 

9. 

10. 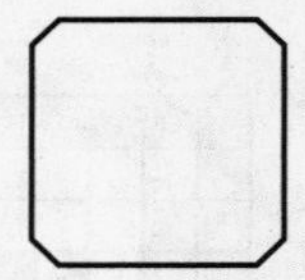

11. 

12. 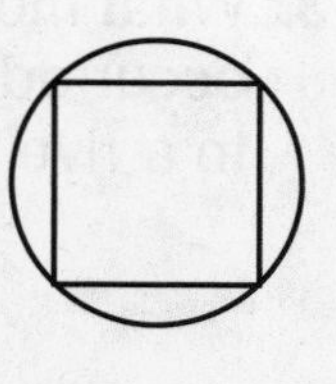

13. 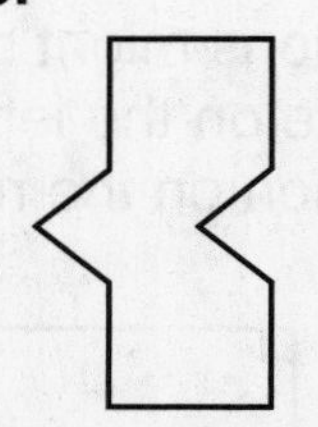

14. 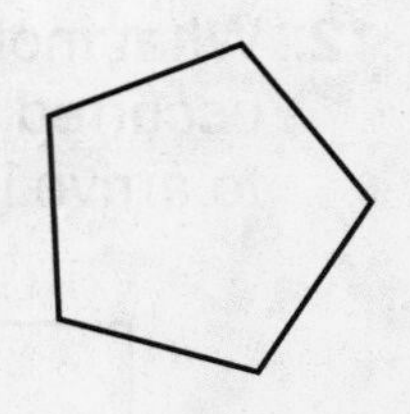

Name: ______

Practice 87

PROBLEM SOLVING: FIND A PATTERN

✔ Read
✔ Plan
✔ Solve
✔ Look Back

Solve using the find-a-pattern strategy.

1. A rectangle has a length of 6 inches, a width of 2 inches, and a perimeter of 16 inches. If 10 of these rectangles were laid end to end, what would the perimeter of the shape be?

6 in.

2 in. | 2 in.

6 in.

______

2. The school needs to know how many rectangular tables to rent for a fundraising dinner. Each table normally seats 6 people—2 on each long side and 1 on each short side. But the school wants to line up all the tables end to end to form one big banquet table that seats 26. How many tables should the school rent?

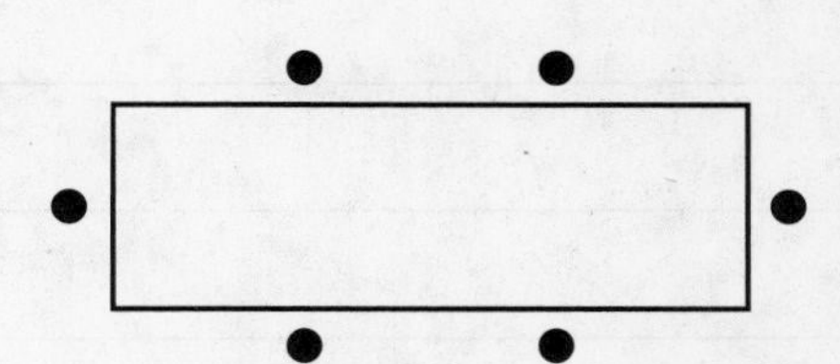

______

3. A graphic artist works for an advertising agency and earns a salary of $3,260 per month. If the agency increases the artist's salary by $50 each month, how many months will it be until the artist is earning $4,010 per month?

______

4. A jewelry designer has 6 gold chains, each consisting of 4 links. If it takes the designer 1 minute to cut a link and 3 minutes to melt the link back together again, how long would it take to change the 6 chains into one long chain?

______

Solve using any method.

5. Suppose there are people and dogs playing in a park. There are 44 legs and 18 heads in the park. The number of heads in the park totals 18. How many people and how many dogs are playing in the park?

______

6. Suppose the fare for a taxi is $4.50 for the first mile and $1.75 for each additional $\frac{1}{2}$ mile. What fare should a passenger who rides for $6\frac{1}{2}$ miles be charged?

______

Name: ______________________________

FUNCTIONS

Complete the table. Describe the function in words and with an equation. Tell what each variable in the equation represents.

1.

pattern number	1	2	3	4	5
picture	•••	••• ••	••• ••• •	••• • ••• • •	••• ••• ••• ••
number of dots	3	5	7	9	11

____

____

____

____

2.

pattern number	1	2	3	4
picture				
number of equal parts	2	4		

____

____

____

____

Write an equation for the function described in words. Tell what each variable in the equation represents.

3. The width of a certain rectangle is $\frac{1}{4}$ its length.

____

____

____

4. The length of a certain rectangle is $2\frac{1}{2}$ times its width.

____

____

____

5. The length in inches of a pencil is equal to 2.54 times its length in centimeters.

____

____

____

____

6. The area of a square is equal to 2 times the length of one side of the square.

____

____

____

____

Name: ____________________

GRAPH FUNCTIONS

Name the coordinates of the point.

1. *B* ________ 2. *Z* ________ 3. *R* ________

4. *Q* ________ 5. *C* ________ 6. *Y* ________

7. *W* ________ 8. *P* ________ 9. *M* ________

10. *K* ________ 11. *L* ________ 12. *V* ________

13. *A* ________ 14. *F* ________ 15. *X* ________

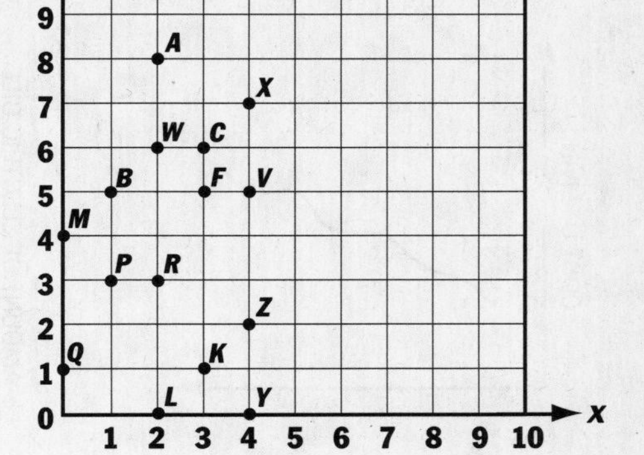

Complete the table for the function represented by the equation. Then graph the function.

16. $a = b$

a	b
1	1
2	
3	
4	

17. $y = x + 2$

x	y
0	2
1	
2	
3	

18. $L = 3W$

L	W
0	
1	
2	
3	

19. $k = 2n - 1$

n	k
1	
2	
3	
4	

20. $y = x + 3$

x	y
1	
3	
5	
7	

21. $y = 2x + 3$

x	y
0	
1	
2	
3	

Solve using the graph for exercises 1–15.

22. Name the coordinate point 2 units down from point *B*.

____

23. Suppose there was a point in between point *Y* and point *Z*. What would its coordinates be?

____

Practice 90

Name: ________________

DESCRIBE CHANGE

Write a story about what each graph shows.

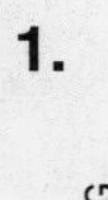

1\.

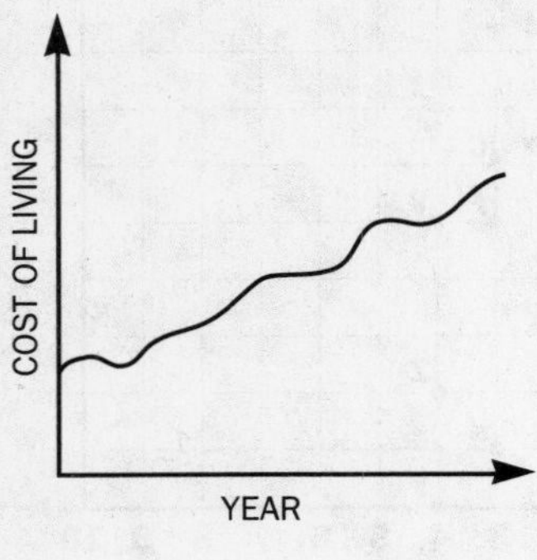

2\.

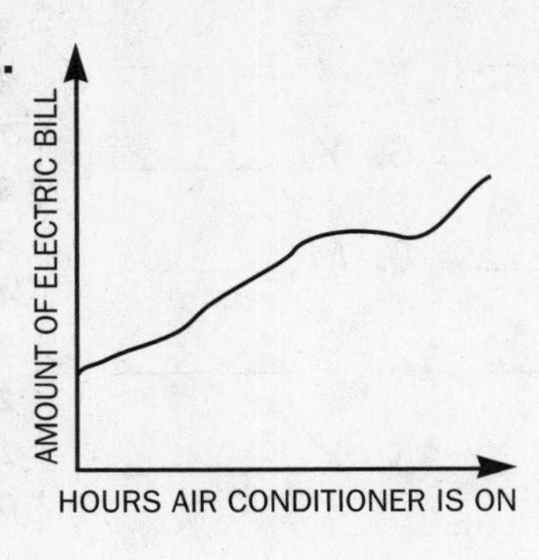

3\.

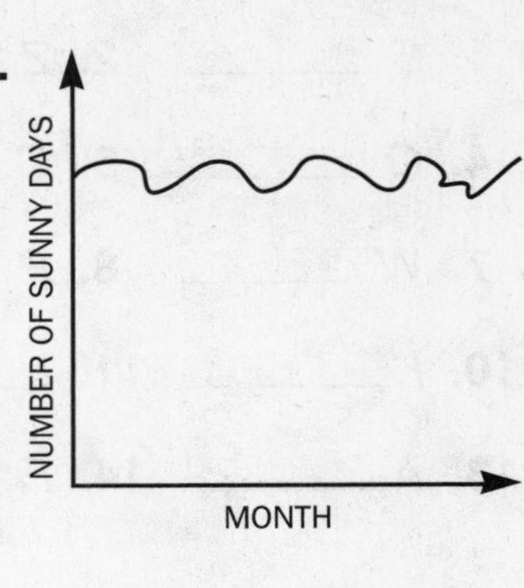

Sketch a graph showing how the quantity on the vertical axis might depend on the quantity on the horizontal axis.

4\.

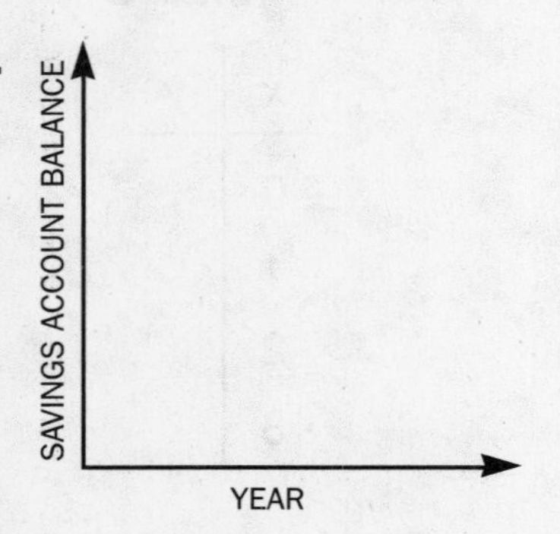

5\.

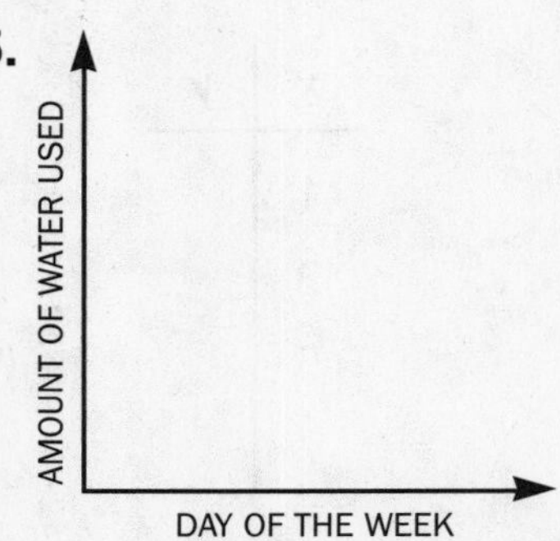

6\.

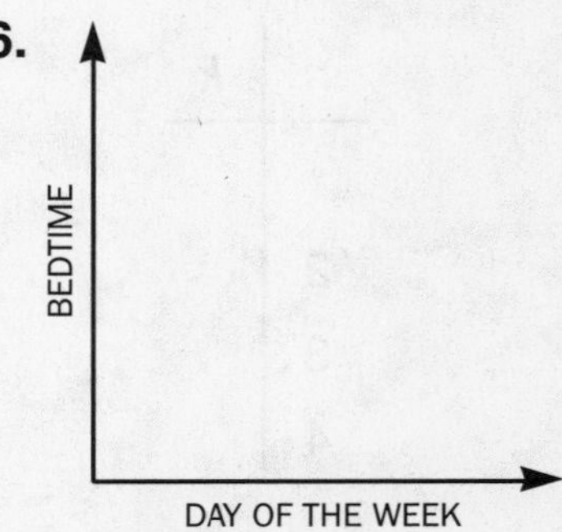

Solve.

7\. Sketch a graph that shows the relationship between the amount of rainfall and the frequency with which a lawn needs to be mowed.

8\. Sketch a graph that shows the relationship between the number of textbooks needed by a class and the number of students in the class.

Name:

USE GRAPHS TO SOLVE PROBLEMS

The graph at the right shows the amount of fuel a car uses for different distances traveled.

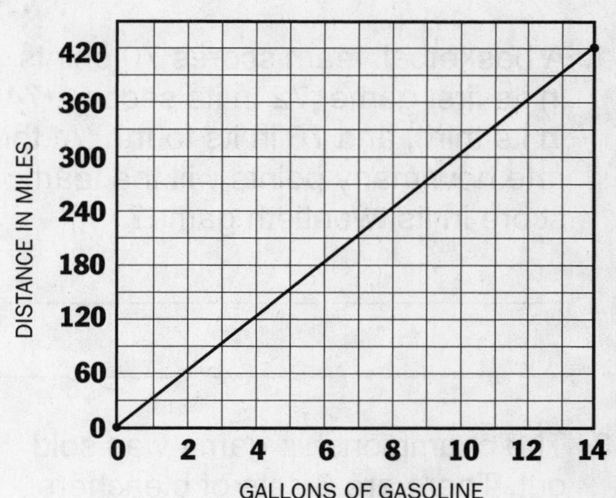

Use the graph to find the number of gallons of gasoline used for each distance.

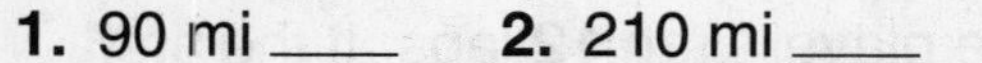

1. 90 mi ____ 2. 210 mi ____

3. 120 mi ____ 4. 270 mi ____

5. 330 mi ____ 6. 300 mi ____

7. 60 mi ____ 8. 150 mi ____

9. 360 mi ____ 10. 180 mi ____

11. How many miles per gallon of gasoline does this car get?

____

Use the graph at the right for problems 12–22.

12. Cost of 2 tickets ________

13. Cost of 9 tickets ________

14. Cost of 5 tickets ________

15. Cost of 12 tickets ________

16. Cost of 7 tickets ________

17. Cost of 11 tickets ________

18. Cost of 8 tickets ________

19. Cost of 3 tickets ________

20. What is the cost of one ticket? ________

21. John needs to buy 14 tickets for his class. How much will this cost him?

____

22. If Amy has $60, how many tickets can she buy?

____

Name: ____________________

PROBLEM-SOLVING STRATEGY: SOLVE SIMPLER PROBLEMS

✔ Read
✔ Plan
✔ Solve
✔ Look Back

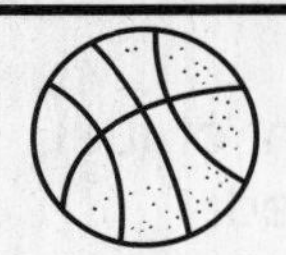

Solve by solving a simpler problem.

1. A basketball team scores 70 points in its first game, 72 in its second, 74 in its third, and 76 in its fourth. At this rate how many points will the team score in its twentieth game?

____

____

2. At the end of every practice, the coach has the players run 2 laps more than the previous practice. If the players ran 12 laps at the first practice, how many laps in total did the 14 players run by the end of the eighteenth practice?

____

3. The championship game was sold out. There are 6 sets of bleachers. Each bleacher has 17 levels. Each level can seat 26 people. How many people were in the bleachers for the final game?

____

4. The basketball court measures 96 feet by 40 feet. Each plank of wood on the court measures 1 foot by 3 inches. How many planks are needed for an entire court?

____

Solve using any method.

5. Amy has 23 customers on her newspaper route. If she delivers one paper every day to each of her customers, about how many papers does she deliver in 1 month?

____

6. Amy rides her bike 5 miles to the printing station to pick up the papers. If she bikes 1 mile in $3\frac{1}{3}$ minutes, how long does it take her to get to the printing station?

____

7. Amy sells the Monday through Friday papers for \$0.35 each, the Saturday paper for \$1.00, and the Sunday paper for \$2.00. How much do 23 subscribers pay in all for one week of delivery?

____

8. Amy earns $\frac{1}{4}$ of what her customers pay her. If her customers pay her about \$400 each month, about how much does Amy earn in one year?

____

Name: ______________________________

Solve Equations

Write the equation for the picture and solve it.

1. 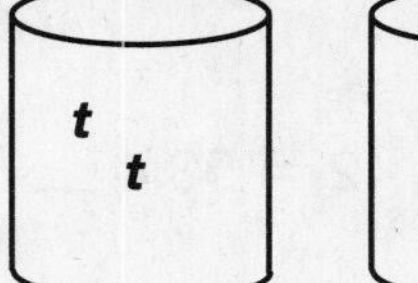

____

2. 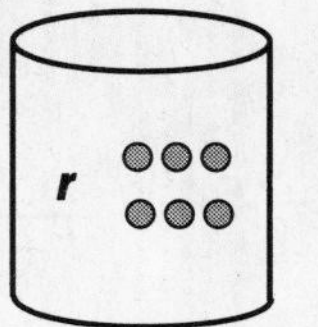

____

3. 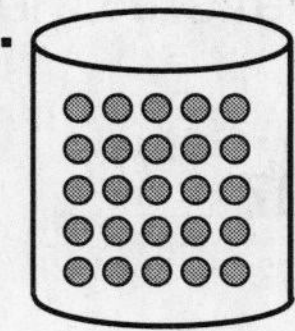

____

4. 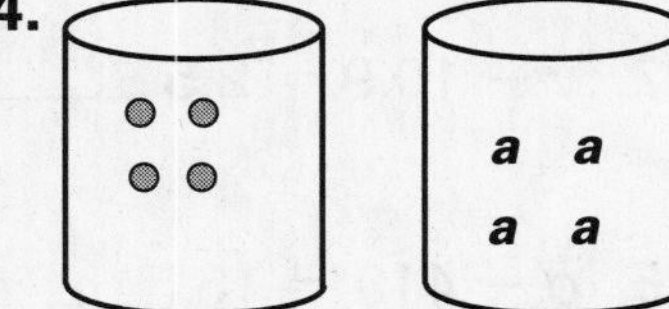

____

5. 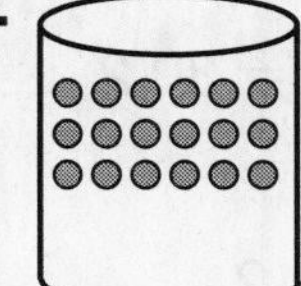

____

6. 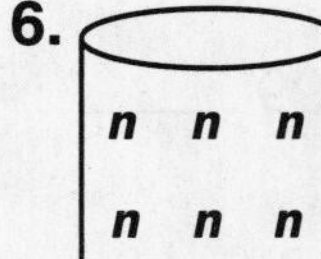

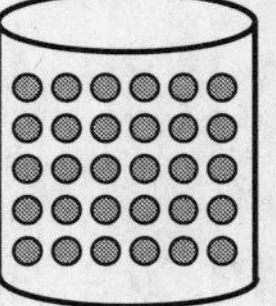

____

Solve each equation. Use any method.

7. $2d = 30$ ____ **8.** $p + 6 = 19$ ____ **9.** $15 = h + 4$ ____ **10.** $36 = 4m$ ____

11. $23 = m + 9$ ____ **12.** $5x = 55$ ____ **13.** $49 = 7s$ ____ **14.** $v + 8 = 25$ ____

15. $q + 5 = 27$ ____ **16.** $48 = 6w$ ____ **17.** $5z = 45$ ____ **18.** $34 = k + 7$ ____

19. $4c = 84$ ____ **20.** $2h = 94$ ____ **21.** $72 = 3d$ ____ **22.** $120 = 6m$ ____

Solve.

23. The area of a rectangle is given by the formula $A = lw$. What is the width of a rectangle that has an area of 216 square inches and a length of 18 inches?

____

24. Name all the possible lengths and widths of a rectangle that has an area of 24 square units. Its length and width are whole numbers.

____

____

Name: ______

Solve Addition and Subtraction Equations

Solve the equation. Check the solution.

1. $n + 9 = 37$ ____
2. $z + 23 = 54$ ____
3. $w + 42 = 53.4$ ____
4. $m + 31.7 = 46$ ____
5. $s - 7 = 15$ ____
6. $h - 18 = 31$ ____
7. $t - 7.3 = 40$ ____
8. $g - 57 = 6.1$ ____
9. $p - 64 = 64$ ____
10. $x + 40 = 99$ ____
11. $c + 19.6 = 30.2$ ____
12. $v - 10.9 = 2.5$ ____
13. $y + 300 = 550$ ____
14. $k - \frac{1}{2} = 12$ ____
15. $q - 410 = 161$ ____
16. $10\frac{1}{2} = j + \frac{1}{8}$ ____
17. $d - 2\frac{3}{4} = 9$ ____
18. $315.03 = z + 247.6$ ____
19. $n - 147.34 = 310.2$ ____
20. $11\frac{3}{5} = r + 10\frac{1}{3}$ ____
21. $24 = h - \frac{2}{5}$ ____

Complete the table.

22.

Rule: $y = x + \frac{1}{2}$	
Input x	Output y
$\frac{1}{4}$	
$\frac{1}{2}$	
$2\frac{3}{8}$	
14	

23.

Rule: $y = x - \frac{1}{4}$	
Input x	Output y
$\frac{3}{4}$	
$\frac{2}{5}$	
$\frac{5}{8}$	
$\frac{7}{16}$	

Name: ______

Practice 95

Solve Multiplication and Division Equations

Solve the equation. Check your solution.

1. $4b = 36$ ______
2. $7x = 63$ ______
3. $40 = 8c$ ______
4. $60 = 10g$ ______
5. $k \div 14 = 4$ ______
6. $6 = \frac{q}{2}$ ______
7. $m \div 13 = 4$ ______
8. $\frac{3}{4}w = 15$ ______
9. $\frac{x}{36} = \frac{1}{3}$ ______
10. $\frac{63}{h} = 9$ ______
11. $p \times \frac{1}{2} = 5$ ______
12. $n \div 3 = 4$ ______
13. $3r = \frac{3}{5}$ ______
14. $y \div 3 = 3\frac{3}{4}$ ______
15. $j \times \frac{2}{5} = 2$ ______
16. $2t = \frac{7}{8}$ ______
17. $y \div 2.5 = 20$ ______
18. $1.2x = 9.6$ ______
19. $4.05v = 44.55$ ______
20. $\frac{k}{3.2} = 9$ ______
21. $b \div 4 = 64$ ______

Complete each table.

22. Rule: $y = 16x$

Input x	Output y
7	
$\frac{3}{8}$	
9.4	

23. Rule: $y = x \div 12$

Input x	Output y
60	
$\frac{2}{3}$	
$1\frac{3}{4}$	

Solve.

24. Lou's science notebook weighs $\frac{1}{8}$ as much as his science textbook. If his science notebook weighs 14 ounces, what is the weight of his science textbook?

______

25. One gallon of water weighs about $8\frac{1}{3}$ pounds. A large aquarium holds 20 gallons of water. About how many pounds of water does the aquarium hold?

______

Name: ______________________________ Practice 96

PROBLEM SOLVING: WORK BACKWARD

✔ Read
✔ Plan
✔ Solve
✔ Look Back

Solve using the work-backward strategy.

1. A community experienced an earthquake that lasted 24 seconds. The earthquake was $\frac{2}{3}$ as long as a previous earthquake the people had experienced. How long was the previous earthquake?

____

2. At 2:20 P.M. a botanist finished an experiment in the forest. It took her 20 minutes to drive to the forest, 45 minutes to set up, and 1 hour and 50 minutes to conduct the experiment. What time did she leave her house?

____

3. A botanist realizes if she multiplies the age of tree 1 by $\frac{1}{2}$, it is the same age as tree 2. If the sum of their ages is 69, how old are tree 1 and tree 2?

____

4. The canopy, or top, of a particular rain forest is 35 meters above the ground. Given that 1 meter = 3.28 feet, find the height of the canopy in feet.

____

Solve using any method.

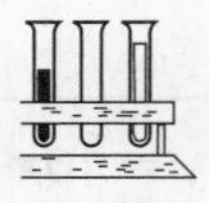

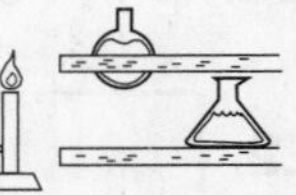

5. In ideal conditions, certain bacteria can divide in half (creating 2 bacteria) every 20 minutes. In ideal conditions, how long would it take one bacterium to number more than 100,000?

____

6. A microbiologist is using a microscope to view two different viruses. The length of one virus is 80 nanometers. The length of the other virus is $3\frac{1}{2}$ times longer. How long is the other virus?

____

7. A scientist estimates that $\frac{9}{10}$ of the experiments she has performed in her career failed to prove a hypothesis. She also estimates she has performed 500 experiments that successfully proved a hypothesis. About how many experiments has the scientist performed in her career?

____

8. About $\frac{2}{5}$ of the weight of the human body is made up of muscles. Estimate the weight of a person if the muscles of that person are estimated to weigh 22 kilograms, and convert the weight to pounds given that 1 kg = 2.205 lb.

____

Name: ____________________

UNDERSTANDING RATIOS

Write a ratio comparing the shaded region to the unshaded region, and a ratio comparing the shaded region to the whole figure.

1. 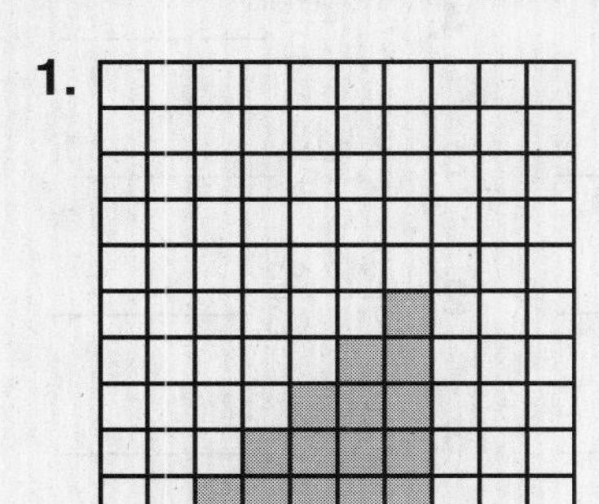

____

2. 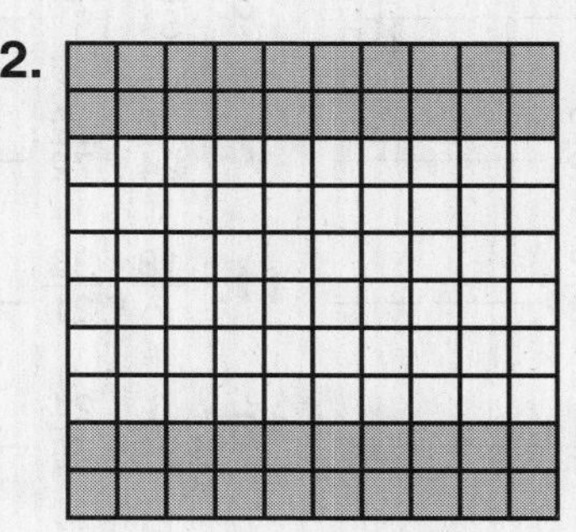

____

3. 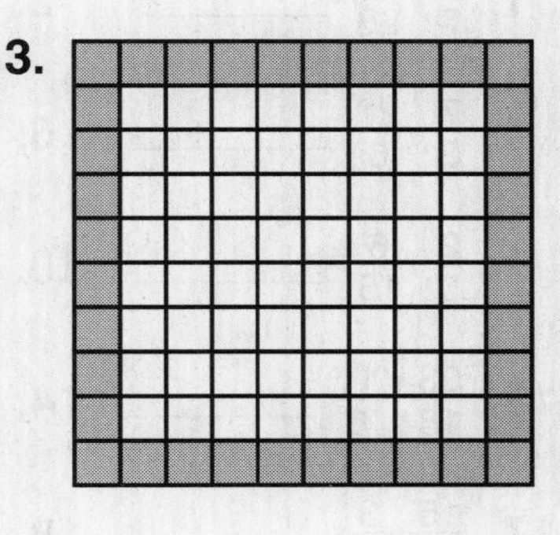

____

Use the survey results to write the ratio in three different ways.

Farm Animals	Number on Farm
horses	4
cows	6
turkeys	1
chickens	22
ducks	8
pigs	14
sheep	13
goats	3

4. horses to cows ______________

5. chickens to pigs ______________

6. sheep to goats ______________

7. turkeys to ducks ______________

8. sheep to pigs ______________

Draw a picture to show each ratio.

9. The ratio of shaded squares to unshaded squares on a 10-by-10 grid is 10 to 90.

10. The ratio of unshaded squares to shaded squares on a 4-by-4 grid is 1 to 3.

11. The ratio of cars to trucks is 8 to 7.

12. The ratio of adults to children is 3 to 4.

13. The ratio of females to males is 5 to 6.

14. The ratio of teachers to students is 1 to 18.

15. The ratio of vowels to consonants is 4 to 9.

16. The ratio of textbooks to students is 1 to 1.

Name:

Equal Ratios

Are the ratios equal? Write *yes* or *no*.

1. $\frac{3}{7}, \frac{12}{28}$ ______ **2.** $\frac{2}{3}, \frac{6}{12}$ ______ **3.** $\frac{3}{5}, \frac{10}{15}$ ______ **4.** $\frac{1}{7}, \frac{6}{42}$ ______

5. $\frac{7}{3}, \frac{21}{6}$ ______ **6.** $\frac{8}{13}, \frac{32}{42}$ ______ **7.** $\frac{10}{24}, \frac{30}{72}$ ______ **8.** $\frac{9}{4}, \frac{18}{8}$ ______

9. $\frac{2}{5}, \frac{6}{15}$ ______ **10.** $\frac{14}{9}, \frac{28}{18}$ ______ **11.** $\frac{18}{7}, \frac{36}{21}$ ______ **12.** $\frac{11}{21}, \frac{33}{63}$ ______

13. $\frac{33}{18}, \frac{11}{6}$ ______ **14.** $\frac{45}{8}, \frac{5}{2}$ ______ **15.** $\frac{6}{36}, \frac{24}{76}$ ______ **16.** $\frac{12}{36}, \frac{3}{5}$ ______

17. $\frac{15}{45}, \frac{3}{9}$ ______ **18.** $\frac{21}{6}, \frac{42}{18}$ ______ **19.** $\frac{25}{5}, \frac{75}{15}$ ______ **20.** $\frac{60}{12}, \frac{10}{2}$ ______

21. $\frac{7}{8}, \frac{35}{40}$ ______ **22.** $\frac{17}{20}, \frac{34}{40}$ ______ **23.** $\frac{4}{5}, \frac{48}{60}$ ______ **24.** $\frac{7}{9}, \frac{42}{45}$ ______

25. $\frac{9}{11}, \frac{81}{88}$ ______ **26.** $\frac{12}{24}, \frac{45}{90}$ ______ **27.** $\frac{6}{7}, \frac{36}{49}$ ______ **28.** $\frac{15}{45}, \frac{1}{3}$ ______

29. $\frac{4}{20}, \frac{12}{60}$ ______ **30.** $\frac{3}{9}, \frac{15}{40}$ ______ **31.** $\frac{28}{21}, \frac{4}{3}$ ______ **32.** $\frac{9}{12}, \frac{81}{108}$ ______

33. $\frac{12}{15}, \frac{48}{50}$ ______ **34.** $\frac{6}{9}, \frac{54}{81}$ ______ **35.** $\frac{34}{64}, \frac{68}{128}$ ______ **36.** $\frac{10}{2}, \frac{100}{20}$ ______

Algebra Find the missing number to make equal ratios.

37. $\frac{1}{2} = \frac{\square}{8}$ **38.** $\frac{\square}{5} = \frac{9}{15}$ **39.** $\frac{7}{4} = \frac{\square}{16}$ **40.** $\frac{8}{24} = \frac{\square}{3}$

41. $\frac{3}{2} = \frac{\square}{12}$ **42.** $\frac{1}{12} = \frac{8}{\square}$ **43.** $\frac{11}{\square} = \frac{66}{12}$ **44.** $\frac{\square}{28} = \frac{24}{7}$

45. $\frac{5}{9} = \frac{25}{\square}$ **46.** $\frac{7}{8} = \frac{\square}{16}$ **47.** $\frac{5}{20} = \frac{\square}{100}$ **48.** $\frac{33}{20} = \frac{99}{\square}$

49. $\frac{21}{3} = \frac{63}{\square}$ **50.** $\frac{1}{30} = \frac{5}{\square}$ **51.** $\frac{16}{32} = \frac{8}{\square}$ **52.** $\frac{65}{25} = \frac{\square}{5}$

53. $\frac{30}{48} = \frac{10}{\square}$ **54.** $\frac{\square}{12} = \frac{6}{2}$ **55.** $\frac{49}{21} = \frac{7}{\square}$ **56.** $\frac{32}{20} = \frac{8}{\square}$

Name: ______________________________

RATES

Find the unit rate.

1. 2,775 miles driven by 3 families =

________ miles driven by 1 family

2. 10 tourists buying 5 souvenirs =

________ tourists buying 1 souvenir

3. 420 miles and 3 rest areas =

________ miles and 1 rest area

4. 128 sightseers in 4 buses =

________ sightseers in 1 bus

5. 2,880 tourists in 960 hotel rooms =

________ tourists in 1 hotel room

6. $501.75 for 3 airline tickets =

________ for 1 airline ticket

7. 2,400 people per 25 square miles =

________ people per 1 square mile

8. 275 miles on 11 gal = ________

miles using 1 gallon

9. 300 mi to 4 in. = ________ mi to 1 in.

10. $120 per 3 days = ________ per day

Algebra Use the rate of 360 miles on 15 gallons to find the missing number for the rate.

11. ________ mi on 45 gal

12. ________ mi on 25 gal

13. ________ mi on 40 gal

14. ________ mi on 5 gal

15. ________ mi on 9 gal

16. ________ mi on 10.5 gal

Solve.

17. The Jackson family drove 792 miles while on vacation. If their car used 44 gallons of gasoline, what was the fuel economy in miles per gallon of the automobile?

____

18. Kansas City, MO, and Atlanta, GA, are 798 miles apart. Suppose it took 1.5 hours to fly an airplane from Kansas City to Atlanta. How many miles did the airplane average per hour?

____

Name: ______________________

Better Buys

Find the unit price. Round to the nearest tenth of a cent if necessary.

1. 2 lb for $3.90 ______________________

2. 3 L for $1.49 ______________________

3. 4 boxes for $2.99 ______________________

4. 10 board feet for $48.00 ______________________

5. 1.5 tons for $600 ______________________

6. 0.5 oz for $22.50 ______________________

Tell which of the two items is the better buy. Explain your reasoning.

7. 10 high-density floppy disks for $7.99 or 100 high-density floppy disks for $69.50

8. 5 pounds of golden delicious apples for $2.59 or 20 pounds of golden delicious apples for $10.99

9. 1 gallon of skim milk for $2.29 or 4 quarts of skim milk for $0.69 per quart

10. 60 fluid ounces of laundry detergent for $3.36 or 100 fluid ounces of the same detergent for $5.60

11. 6 eggs for $0.89 or 12 for $1.49

12. 36 oranges for $3.69 or 6 oranges for $0.65

13. A box of 8 cereal bars for $3.69 or a box of 24 cereal bars for $8.49

14. 5 cheese sticks for $2.49 or 12 cheese sticks for $5.29

Practice 101

Name: ____________________

PROPORTIONS

Do the ratios form a proportion? Write *yes* or *no*.

1. $\frac{1}{2}$ and $\frac{4}{8}$ ______
2. $\frac{1}{6}$ and $\frac{5}{30}$ ______
3. $\frac{12}{14}$ and $\frac{5}{7}$ ______
4. $\frac{15}{6}$ and $\frac{45}{25}$ ______
5. $\frac{8}{11}$ and $\frac{24}{44}$ ______
6. $\frac{9}{16}$ and $\frac{36}{64}$ ______
7. $\frac{4}{26}$ and $\frac{2}{13}$ ______
8. $\frac{5}{3}$ and $\frac{45}{27}$ ______
9. $\frac{4}{7}$ and $\frac{8}{10}$ ______
10. $\frac{5}{9}$ and $\frac{25}{45}$ ______
11. $\frac{3}{6}$ and $\frac{6}{10}$ ______
12. $\frac{11}{22}$ and $\frac{1}{2}$ ______
13. $\frac{9}{8}$ and $\frac{3}{2}$ ______
14. $\frac{4}{7}$ and $\frac{24}{28}$ ______
15. $\frac{5}{8}$ and $\frac{40}{64}$ ______
16. $\frac{7}{8}$ and $\frac{49}{56}$ ______
17. $\frac{6}{13}$ and $\frac{12}{26}$ ______
18. $\frac{16}{40}$ and $\frac{32}{80}$ ______
19. $\frac{14}{16}$ and $\frac{28}{40}$ ______
20. $\frac{8}{12}$ and $\frac{16}{32}$ ______
21. $\frac{9}{4}$ and $\frac{36}{12}$ ______
22. $\frac{12}{20}$ and $\frac{24}{42}$ ______
23. $\frac{75}{90}$ and $\frac{15}{16}$ ______
24. $\frac{2.1}{14}$ and $\frac{8.4}{56}$ ______
25. $\frac{5}{3.4}$ and $\frac{2.5}{1.65}$ ______
26. $\frac{2}{0.5}$ and $\frac{16}{4}$ ______
27. $\frac{6.5}{2}$ and $\frac{26}{2}$ ______

Algebra Solve.

28. $\frac{2}{3} = \frac{b}{6}$ ______
29. $\frac{3}{5} = \frac{15}{x}$ ______
30. $\frac{7}{r} = \frac{21}{12}$ ______
31. $\frac{y}{8} = \frac{12}{32}$ ______
32. $\frac{9}{w} = \frac{54}{12}$ ______
33. $\frac{k}{12} = \frac{15}{36}$ ______
34. $\frac{12}{11} = \frac{s}{66}$ ______
35. $\frac{9}{15} = \frac{p}{60}$ ______
36. $\frac{21}{5} = \frac{84}{z}$ ______
37. $\frac{12}{17} = \frac{m}{68}$ ______
38. $\frac{d}{10} = \frac{15}{25}$ ______
39. $\frac{14}{h} = \frac{21}{27}$ ______
40. $\frac{9}{6} = \frac{81}{a}$ ______
41. $\frac{b}{8} = \frac{2.25}{6}$ ______
42. $\frac{45}{9} = \frac{e}{11}$ ______
43. $\frac{g}{5} = \frac{7}{35}$ ______
44. $\frac{12}{6} = \frac{10}{n}$ ______
45. $\frac{18}{8} = \frac{27}{n}$ ______
46. $\frac{k}{68} = \frac{8}{17}$ ______
47. $\frac{16}{g} = \frac{80}{30}$ ______
48. $\frac{12}{20} = \frac{r}{35}$ ______
49. $\frac{5}{3.4} = \frac{2.5}{t}$ ______
50. $\frac{2.6}{s} = \frac{7.8}{1.5}$ ______
51. $\frac{a}{2.4} = \frac{26}{52}$ ______
52. $\frac{8}{c} = \frac{64}{4}$ ______
53. $\frac{2.5}{5} = \frac{x}{10}$ ______
54. $\frac{y}{2} = \frac{11}{5}$ ______

Name: ______________________________

PROBLEM-SOLVING STRATEGY: WRITE AN EQUATION

✔ Read
✔ Plan
✔ Solve
✔ Look Back

Solve using the write-an-equation strategy.

1. A guitar shop sells an average of 1 guitar every 5 days. How many does it sell in 5 months?

2. A guitar shop displays guitars in rows of 4. There are 5 rows of guitars along 4 walls of the store. How many guitars are on display?

3. A guitar teacher gives lessons 6 times a day for 5 days each week. How many lessons does she give in 6 months?

4. Guitar lessons cost $15 an hour. Tara pays a total of $120 at the end of four weeks. How many lessons does she take each week?

Solve using any method.

5. A suitcase contains 4 blouses and 3 pairs of slacks. If any blouse can be worn with any pair of slacks, how many different combinations of blouses and slacks can be worn?

6. Elaine swims about 2 hours each day and spends 2 hours playing tennis. If her vacation lasts one week, how many hours does Elaine spend swimming and playing tennis?

7. An odometer records distance traveled. At the beginning of a vacation, an automobile odometer read 32,416.4 miles. At the end of the vacation, the odometer read 34,050.7 miles. How many miles were driven during the vacation?

8. While preparing for a vacation, the Anders family packed 6 suitcases. Each member of the family carries about 25 pounds of luggage. How many pounds of luggage do they carry altogether?

Name: ______________________________

Similar Figures

In the picture at the right, triangle $BCD \sim PQR$. Find the corresponding side or angle.

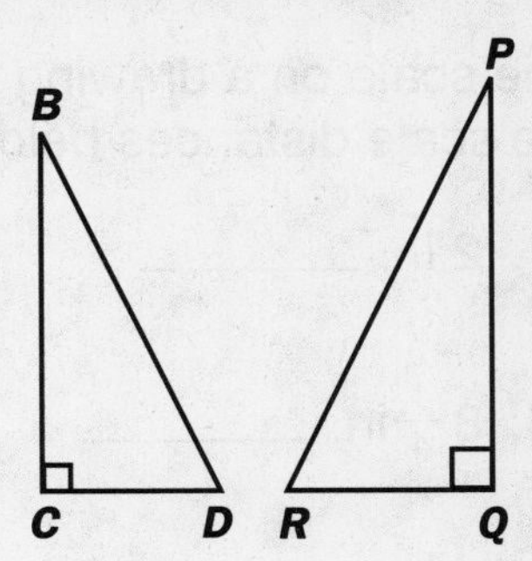

1. $\overline{BD}$ ________ 2. $\overline{CB}$ ________ 3. $\overline{QR}$ ________

4. $\angle P$ ________ 5. $\angle C$ ________ 6. $\angle R$ ________

Algebra The figures in the pair are similar. Solve for x.

7.

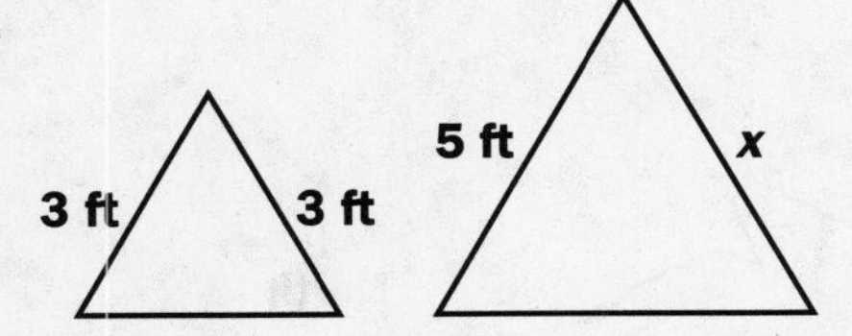

____

8.

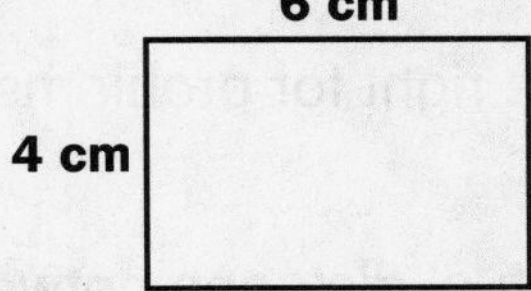

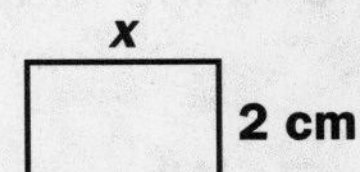

____

9.

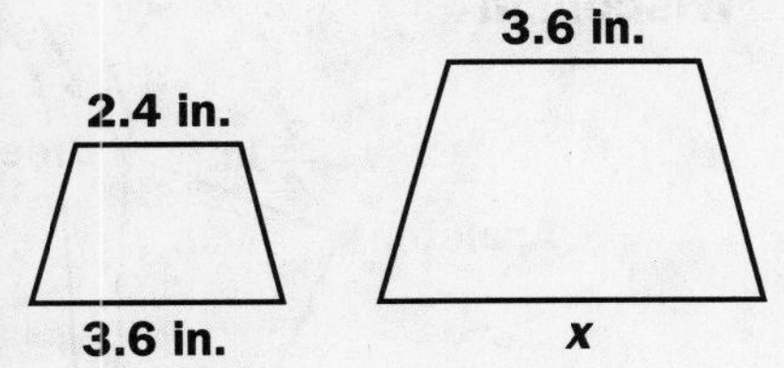

____

10.

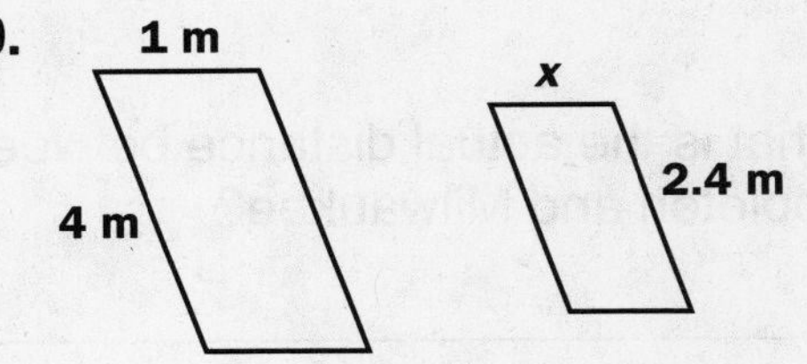

____

11.

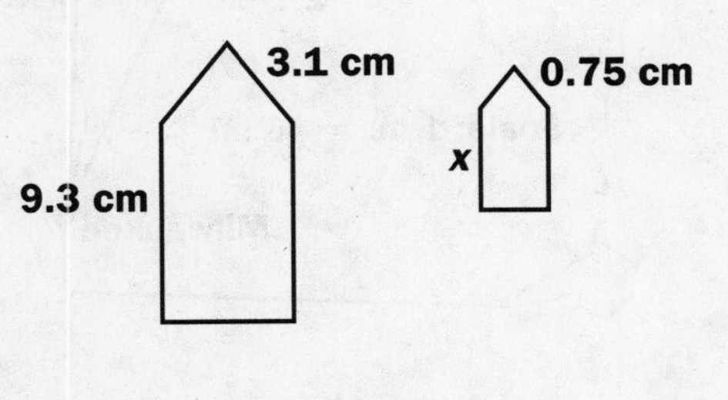

____

12.

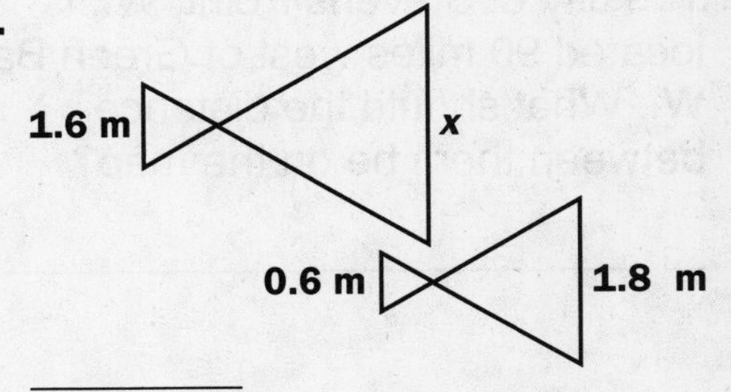

____

Solve.

13. A rectangle has a length of 12.6 m and a width of 6.3 m. A similar rectangle has a width of 2.1 m. What is the length of the similar rectangle?

____

14. A rectangle has a length of 16 inches and a width of 6 inches. A similar rectangle has a length of 24 inches. What is the width of the similar rectangle?

____

Name: ____________________

SCALE DRAWINGS

The scale on a drawing is 1 in. = 4 ft. Find the actual distances for the scale distances below.

1. 2 in. ________ **2.** $\frac{1}{2}$ in. ________ **3.** 5 in. ________

4. $8\frac{1}{4}$ in. ________ **5.** $10\frac{3}{4}$ in. ________ **6.** $1\frac{1}{2}$ in. ________

Use the map at the right for problems 7–9.

7. What is the actual distance between Milwaukee and Green Bay?

____

8. What is the actual distance between Appleton and Milwaukee?

____

9. The city of Stevens Point, WI, is located 90 miles west of Green Bay, WI. What should the distance between them be on the map?

____

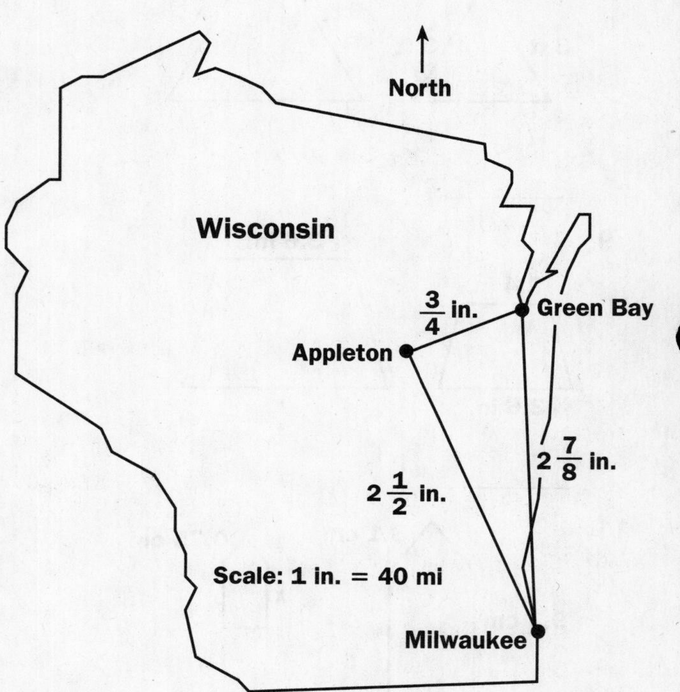

Solve.

10. A model for a house uses a scale of 1 in. = 8 ft. If the walls of a room in the model measure 1 in. long by 2 in. wide, what will the actual measurements of the wall be?

____

11. A model for a house uses a scale of 1 cm = 2 m. If the height of the actual room measures 2.5 m, how many centimeters high is the model?

____

Name: ______

Practice 105

Problem Solving: Solve Multistep Problems

✔ Read
✔ Plan
✔ Solve
✔ Look Back

Solve.

1. An oceanfront house rents for $350 a week during July and $300 a week during August. If a family rents the house for 2 weeks in July and 3 weeks in August, what is the total amount the family will pay?

______

2. A grandfather took his three grandchildren on a vacation. The airplane flight for each grandchild costs $220. The grandfather received a senior citizen's discount of 10% on his ticket. How much money did the grandfather spend on the flight?

______

3. Paddleboats are rented for $6.50 per hour. A couple rented a paddleboat for 2 hours in the morning and again in the evening for $1\frac{1}{2}$ hours. What was the total cost for renting a paddleboat that day?

______

4. On Saturday, David skied a trail measuring 0.45 miles six different times, a trail measuring 0.62 miles four different times, and a trail measuring 0.9 miles once. How many miles did David ski altogether on Saturday?

______

Solve using any method.

5. The regular rise and fall of water in a river, lake, or ocean is called the tide. At 2 P.M., the tide measured 46 inches. At 4 P.M., the tide measured 38 inches. Estimate the time of day the tide measured 40 inches.

______

6. Linda and her friend Latoya skied a cross-country ski trail measuring 1,780 m in length and another measuring 2.6 km in length. Which trail was longer? How much longer was it?

______

7. Suppose a boat has 10 gallons of fuel on board and uses 3 gallons of fuel per hour. In how many hours and minutes would you expect the boat to run out of fuel?

______

8. Myron enjoys watching birds. While on vacation, he estimates that he identified 10 different bird species every day. If he vacationed for 12 days, about how many different species did he identify altogether?

______

Name: ______________________________

PERCENT

Shade the grid to show the fraction, ratio, or decimal. Tell what percent is shaded.

1. 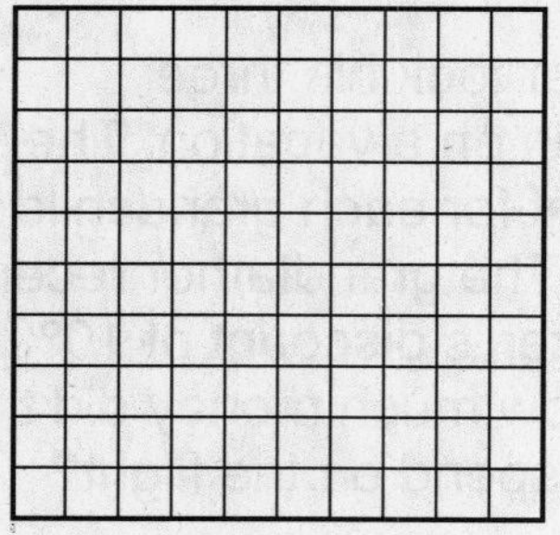

$\frac{11}{100}$ ______

2. 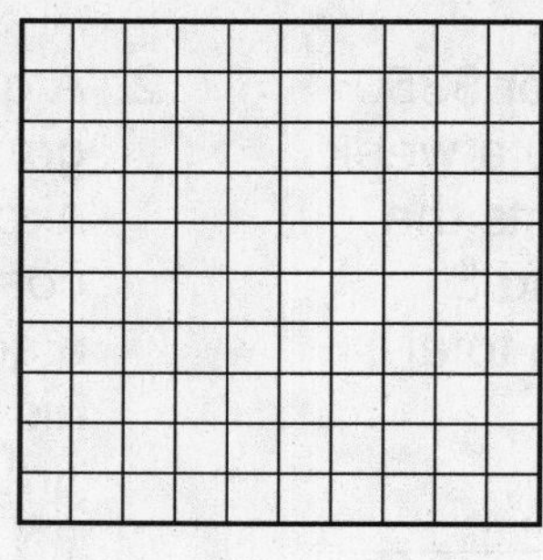

5:10 ______

3. 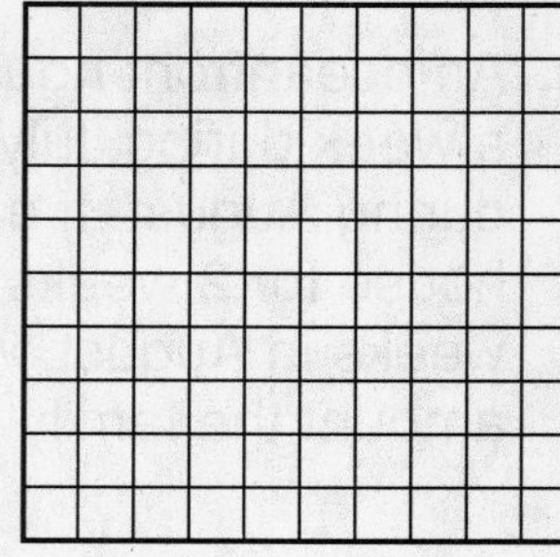

0.28 ______

4. 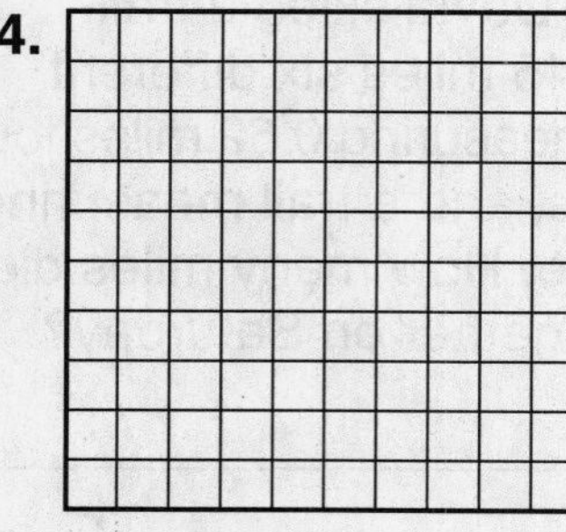

$\frac{7}{20}$ ______

5. 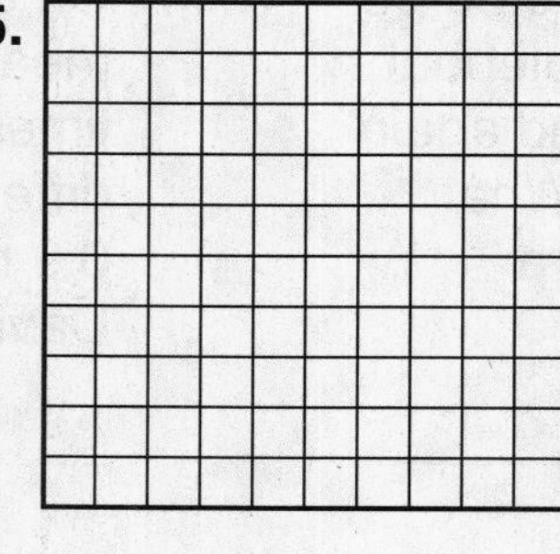

43:100 ______

6. 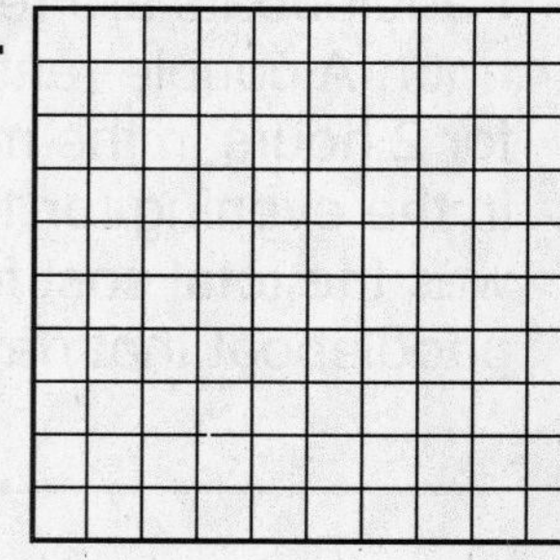

0.8 ______

Write the fraction, ratio, or decimal as a percent. You may use a model to help you.

7. 0.4 ______ **8.** $\frac{2}{10}$ ______ **9.** 13:100 ______ **10.** 0.35 ______

11. $\frac{1}{4}$ ______ **12.** 23:100 ______ **13.** 0.46 ______ **14.** $\frac{63}{100}$ ______

15. 32:100 ______ **16.** 0.96 ______ **17.** 18:100 ______ **18.** 0.12 ______

19. $\frac{75}{100}$ ______ **20.** $\frac{2}{4}$ ______ **21.** $\frac{7}{10}$ ______ **22.** 10:100 ______

23. $\frac{69}{100}$ ______ **24.** $\frac{25}{100}$ ______ **25.** 0.19 ______ **26.** $\frac{4}{5}$ ______

Solve.

27. One fourth of the students in a sixth grade class walk to and from school each day. What percent of the class walks to and from school each day?

____

28. A workbook contains 100 lessons. Nicole has completed 53 of the lessons. What percent of the lessons has Nicole completed?

____

Name: ______

PERCENT, FRACTIONS, AND DECIMALS

Write the percent as a fraction in simplest form and as a decimal.

1. 7% ______ 2. 91% ______ 3. 9% ______ 4. 2% ______

5. 20% ______ 6. 48% ______ 7. 34% ______ 8. 65% ______

9. 80% ______ 10. 75% ______ 11. 24% ______ 12. 61% ______

13. 12% ______ 14. 54% ______ 15. 72% ______ 16. 26% ______

17. 82% ______ 18. 96% ______ 19. 85% ______ 20. 62% ______

Write the fraction or decimal as a percent.

21. $\frac{17}{100}$ ______ 22. $\frac{7}{10}$ ______ 23. $\frac{1}{4}$ ______ 24. $\frac{3}{10}$ ______

25. $\frac{9}{10}$ ______ 26. $\frac{11}{20}$ ______ 27. $\frac{35}{50}$ ______ 28. $\frac{7}{25}$ ______

29. $\frac{19}{20}$ ______ 30. $\frac{17}{25}$ ______ 31. $\frac{42}{50}$ ______ 32. $\frac{2}{5}$ ______

33. $\frac{3}{50}$ ______ 34. $\frac{21}{25}$ ______ 35. $\frac{16}{20}$ ______ 36. 0.65 ______

37. 0.52 ______ 38. 0.36 ______ 39. 0.05 ______ 40. 0.46 ______

41. 0.6 ______ 42. 0.18 ______ 43. 0.70 ______ 44. 0.54 ______

45. 0.35 ______ 46. 0.03 ______ 47. 0.92 ______ 48. 0.01 ______

Solve.

49. In a survey, 15 out of 50 students chose Friday as their favorite school day. What percent of students is that?

______

50. In a class of 25 students, 10 said their favorite school day is Thursday. What percent of students is that?

______

Name: ____________________

PERCENT OF A NUMBER

Find the percent of each number. You may use a model to help.

1. 20% of 40 ______	**2.** 10% of 30 ______	**3.** 25% of 20 ______
4. 50% of 80 ______	**5.** 20% of 50 ______	**6.** 25% of 8 ______
7. 10% of 60 ______	**8.** 50% of 70 ______	**9.** 10% of 70 ______
10. 20% of 80 ______	**11.** 10% of 50 ______	**12.** 10% of 90 ______
13. 10% of 20 ______	**14.** 30% of 60 ______	**15.** 50% of 24 ______
16. 20% of 20 ______	**17.** 20% of 85 ______	**18.** 50% of 50 ______
19. 10% of 40 ______	**20.** 20% of 45 ______	**21.** 25% of 60 ______
22. 20% of 90 ______	**23.** 20% of 75 ______	**24.** 25% of 40 ______
25. 50% of 36 ______	**26.** 20% of 65 ______	**27.** 30% of 20 ______
28. 25% of 80 ______	**29.** 25% of 100 ______	**30.** 20% of 35 ______
31. 25% of 140 ______	**32.** 50% of 20 ______	**33.** 25% of 72 ______
34. 50% of 96 ______	**35.** 20% of 120 ______	**36.** 25% of 160 ______
37. 25% of 120 ______	**38.** 50% of 270 ______	**39.** 10% of 110 ______
40. 20% of 185 ______	**41.** 20% of 230 ______	**42.** 25% of 300 ______
43. 10% of 310 ______	**44.** 25% of 508 ______	**45.** 10% of 280 ______
46. 20% of 225 ______	**47.** 25% of 260 ______	**48.** 50% of 190 ______
49. 20% of 145 ______	**50.** 50% of 132 ______	**51.** 10% of 240 ______

Solve.

52. A clothing store is having a sale. A sweater at the store that once cost $32 is marked down 25%. How much is taken off the cost of the sweater?

____

53. A discount store manager estimates that 10% of customers leave the store without purchasing anything. If an average of 150 customers visit the store each hour, how many customers each hour do not purchase anything?

____

Name: ____________________ **Practice 109**

PERCENT OF A NUMBER

Find the percent of the number. Round to the nearest hundredth or nearest cent if necessary.

1. 30% of 50 ______ **2.** 10% of $14 ______ **3.** 40% of 60 ______

4. 100% of 24 ______ **5.** 25% of 48 ______ **6.** 50% of 64 ______

7. 10% of 50 ______ **8.** 65% of 60 ______ **9.** 2% of 30 ______

10. 20% of 80 ______ **11.** 45% of 40 ______ **12.** 30% of 60 ______

13. 55% of 100 ______ **14.** 4% of $25 ______ **15.** 5% of $30 ______

16. 3% of 20 ______ **17.** 92% of 200 ______ **18.** 20% of $3.20 ______

19. 8% of $23.90 ______ **20.** 5% of 25 ______ **21.** 50% of $21.25 ______

22. 14% of $34.38 ______ **23.** 6% of 150 ______ **24.** 3% of $2.28 ______

Algebra Complete the table.

25.

n	10				
20% of n	2	4	6	8	10

26.

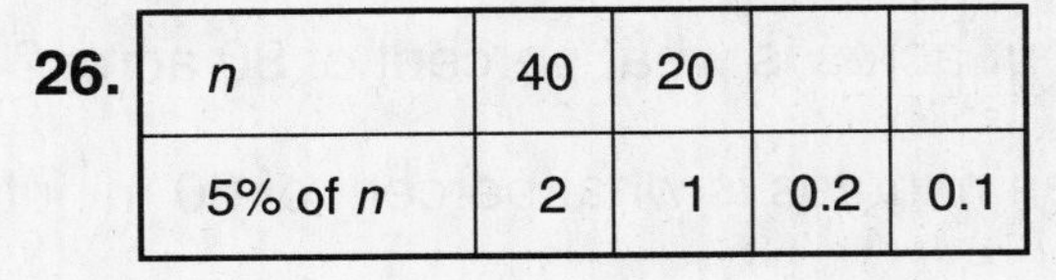

n	40	20		
5% of n	2	1	0.2	0.1

Solve.

27. Julie spends $12 a month on cat food. If the sales tax is 6%, how much is her total bill?

____

28. Julie buys herself a shirt and shoes for $35. The sales tax on clothes is 4%. What is the total cost of her purchase?

____

Practice 110

Name: ____________________

Percent One Number Is of Another

Find the percent. Round decimals to the nearest hundredth if necessary.

1. 24 is what percent of 40? ______
2. 48 is what percent of 60? ______
3. 15 is what percent of 20? ______
4. 16 is what percent of 32? ______
5. 20 is what percent of 200? ______
6. 33 is what percent of 60? ______
7. 64 is what percent of 96? ______
8. 85 is what percent of 120? ______
9. 28 is what percent of 35? ______
10. 67 is what percent of 94? ______
11. 85 is what percent of 105? ______
12. 45 is what percent of 81? ______
13. What percent of 60 is 21? ______
14. What percent of 80 is 24? ______
15. What percent of 120 is 42? ______
16. What percent of 200 is 50? ______
17. What percent of 300 is 15? ______
18. What percent of 200 is 10? ______
19. What percent of 80 is 16? ______
20. What percent of 65 is 52? ______
21. What percent of 180 is 60? ______
22. What percent of 85 is 13? ______
23. What percent of 230 is 80? ______
24. What percent of 240 is 60? ______
25. What percent of 6 pounds is 2 pounds? ______
26. Four acres is what percent of 80 acres? ______
27. Ten minutes is what percent of 60 minutes? ______
28. What percent of $105 is $30? ______

Solve.

29. A teacher reported that during the first half of the school year, 21 students had perfect attendance. If the class has 30 students altogether, what percent of the class had perfect attendance?

____

30. A survey of 40 sixth graders found that 12 students studied more than one hour for a quiz. What percent of the students studied for more than one hour?

____

Name: ______________________

Discounts

Find the discount and sale price. Round to the nearest cent if necessary.

1. Regular price: $4
   Discount: 15%
   ____

2. Regular price: $16
   Discount: 10%
   ____

3. Regular price: $18
   Discount: 20%
   ____

4. Regular price: $25
   Discount: 25%
   ____

5. Regular price: $60
   Discount: 40%
   ____

6. Regular price: $75
   Discount: 30%
   ____

7. Regular price: $3.79
   Discount: 10%
   ____

8. Regular price: $7.39
   Discount: 15%
   ____

9. Regular price: $12.49
   Discount: 20%
   ____

10. Regular price: $32.99
    Discount: 25%
    ____

11. Regular price: $48.89
    Discount: 30%
    ____

12. Regular price: $79.99
    Discount: 40%
    ____

Find the cost of each item on sale.

Computer Sale
All Computers 10% off
All Accessories 15% off
All Software 20% off

13. An accessory keyboard cover originally priced at $11.49 ________

14. A software game CD originally priced at $29.99 ________

15. An accessory mouse pad originally priced at $6.95 ________

Solve. Round to the nearest cent where necessary.

16. A store discounts school supplies by 25%. The regular price of a spiral notebook is $1.69. What is the sale price?
    ____

17. Another store discounts school supplies by 30%. The regular price of a box of 12 pencils is $1.95. What is the sale price of the box?
    ____

Name: ______________________________

Problem-Solving Strategy: Use Alternate Solution Methods

✔ Read
✔ Plan
✔ Solve
✔ Look Back

Solve.

1. A restaurant offers a 15% discount to senior citizens. A group of seniors ordered lunches and beverages totaling $15.80. How much will the group's meals cost? Show two ways to solve the problem.

____

____

____

2. A bedspread at a department store costs $36.50. It is on sale for 20% off. What is the cost of the bedspread? Show two ways to solve the problem.

____

____

____

____

3. A selection of tools purchased at a hardware store costs $78.15. There is a discount of 10% for orders over $75.00. A 3% sales tax was applied to the order. What was the total cost?

____

4. Bus tokens cost $1.50 each. A savings of 10% can be realized if 10 or more tokens are purchased at one time. Find the cost of purchasing 20 tokens.

____

Solve using any method.

TUESDAY LUNCH SPECIAL	
Enchilada	$3.90
Taco	$1.25
Fajita	$2.50
Tamale	$2.00
Frijoles	$2.25

5. On Tuesday, Gwen and Lita shared an enchilada lunch. If they split the cost of the lunch equally, what was each person's cost?

____

6. For lunch on Tuesday, Mario ordered frijoles for himself and a fajita for his friend Ken. What did the order cost?

____

7. Tino ate two fajitas and a tamale. How much did he spend?

____

Name: ______________________________

Interpret and Make Circle Graphs

Use the circle graph for problems 1–4.

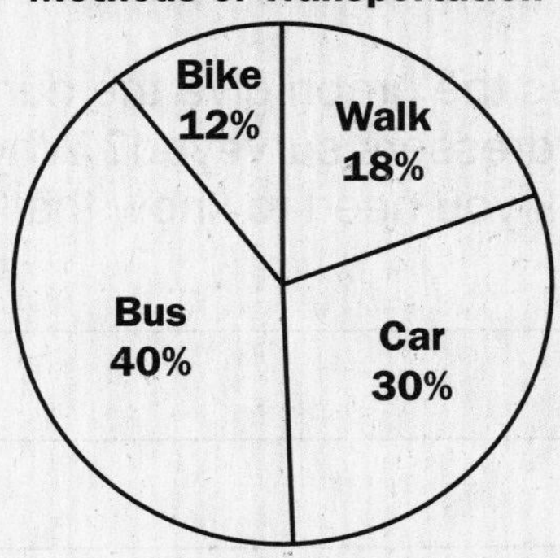

1. Do more students travel by bus or by car?

____

2. About what fraction of the students walk to school?

____

3. If there were 30 students surveyed, how many travel by bus?

____

4. What method of transportation does the fewest number of students use?

____

Solve.

5. Make a circle graph that displays the data in the table at the right.

STUDENTS' FAVORITE FRUITS	
apples	20%
oranges	28%
bananas	4%
grapefruit	12%
watermelon	24%
strawberries	12%

6. Which two fruits were the most popular?

____

7. If there were 40 students surveyed, how many said apples were their favorite fruit?

____

8. If there were 40 students surveyed, about how many students said watermelon was their favorite fruit?

____

Name: ______________________________

PROBLEM SOLVING: INTERPRET DATA

✔ Read
✔ Plan
✔ Solve
✔ Look Back

Use the graph to solve problems 1–3.

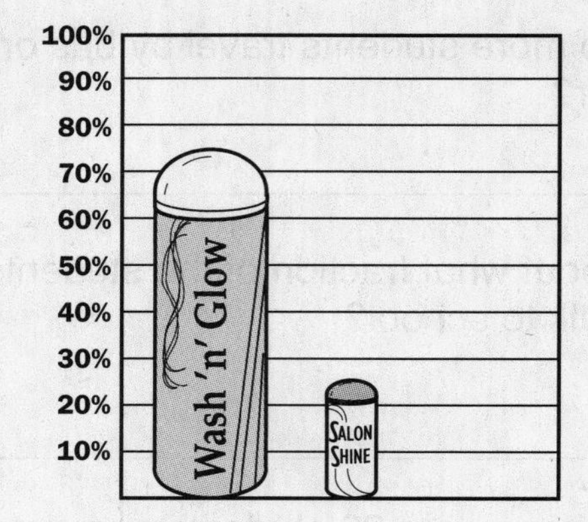

1. Does the graph give the number of hairdressers surveyed? Why do you think you need to know that?

2. How many brand names were given as choices for the hairdressers who were surveyed? As a customer, would you want to know whether the hairdressers recommended other brand names?

3. What does the graph tell you? Is there anything about the graph that is misleading?

4. Car windshield wipers are on sale for 20% off. They normally cost $5 a pair. How much will Jill save if she buys one pair?

5. Jim buys 3 cans of car wax for $4.50 each. How much does he pay if he buys 2 and gets one free?

Name: ______________________

PROBABILITY

Suppose you select a cube from the bag without looking. Find the probability.

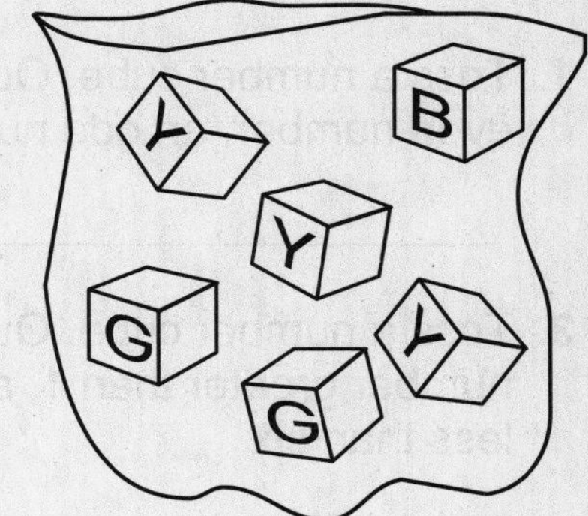

1. P(brown) ______ 2. P(yellow) ______

3. P(green or yellow) ______ 4. P(not green) ______

5. P(green or brown) ______ 6. P(green) ______

Suppose that after mixing the cards, you choose one without looking, record the outcome, and put it back. Find the probability.

M	Q	C	A	X

7. P(C or Q) ______ 8. P(not X or M) ______

9. P(a vowel) ______ 10. P(a consonant) ______

Suppose you spin the spinner. Find the probability.

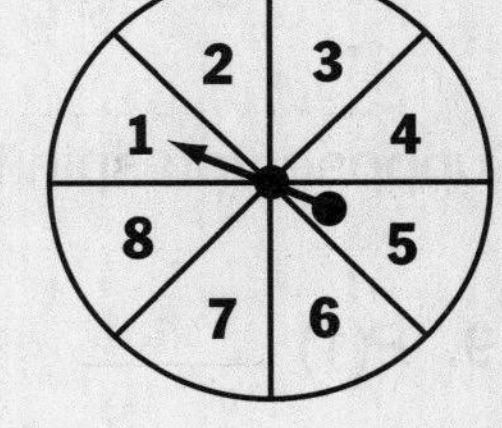

11. P(6) ______ 12. P(an odd number) ______

13. P(9) ______ 14. P(not 3, 4, or 6) ______

15. P(number greater than 4) ______ 16. P(4 or 8) ______

17. P(number greater than 2) ______ 18. P(1, 2, 3, 4, 5, 6, 7, or 8) ______

Solve.

19. What is the probability that a coin will land heads up when tossed?

____

20. What is the probability that you were born on a Wednesday?

____

Name: ____________________

Practice 116

PROBABILITY

For the experiment, tell whether the outcomes listed are equally likely. If they are not equally likely, tell which is the most likely.

1. Toss a number cube. Outcomes: an even number, an odd number

   ____

2. Spin a spinner that is half red and half blue. Outcome: red, green

   ____

3. Toss a number cube. Outcomes: a number greater than 1, a number less than six

   ____

4. Look at the letters of the alphabet. Outcomes: a person's name begins with a vowel, begins with a consonant

   ____

   ____

Suppose you choose a cube from the bag without looking. Find the probability.

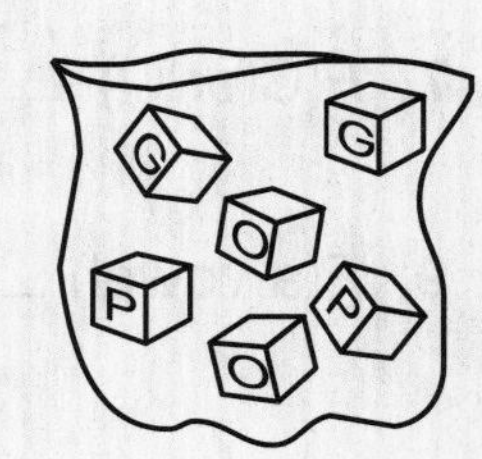

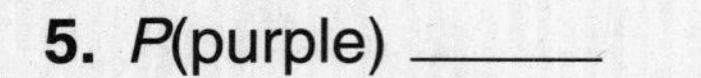

5. *P*(purple) ______
6. *P*(orange or gray) ______
7. *P*(not gray) ______
8. *P*(purple, gray, or orange) ______

Suppose you spin the spinner at the right. Find the probability.

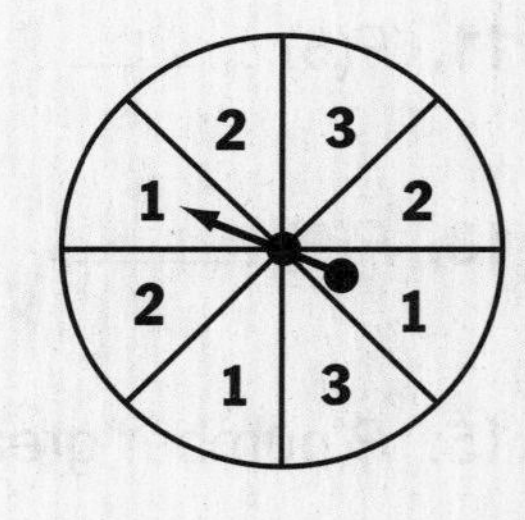

9. *P*(1) ______
10. *P*(4) ______
11. *P*(not 1 or 3) ______
12. *P*(not 3) ______
13. *P*(1, 2, or 3) ______
14. *P*(not 1 or 2) ______

Solve.

15. A coin purse contains 6 dimes. Two were minted in 1996. What is the probability of reaching into the purse, not looking, and choosing a dime minted in 1996?

    ____

16. A drawer contains 16 loose socks. Ten are not white. What is the probability of reaching into the drawer, not looking, and choosing a white sock?

    ____

Name:

Practice 117

Problem-Solving Strategy: Use a Simulation

✔ Read
✔ Plan
✔ Solve
✔ Look Back

Solve by using a simulation.

1. Suppose a quiz has 25 true/false questions. Use a simulation to find the probability of correctly guessing the answer to all the questions.

2. A family has 4 children. Use a simulation to find the probability that the first 2 children were girls and the last 2 children were boys.

3. Suppose a multiple-choice quiz has 2 questions. Each question has 6 possible choices—A, B, C, D, E, or F. The correct answers have been assigned randomly. Use a simulation to find the probability that choice A is the correct answer for each question.

4. Three number cubes are tossed at the same time. Use a simulation to find the probability that the outcome of each cube is an even number.

Name: ____

MAKE PREDICTIONS

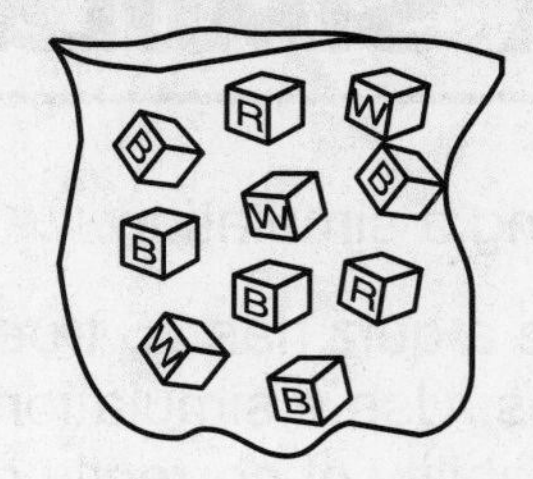

Predict the number of times you would get each color if you did this experiment 100 times.

Experiment: Without looking, take a cube from the bag, write down its color, and then put it back.

1. red ________ **2.** blue ________ **3.** white or red ________

4. not white ________ **5.** blue or white ________ **6.** white ________

Predict the number of residents who would vote for each candidate.

Survey: A random sample of 100 residents of a city of 2,400 people were asked who they would vote for in a mayoral election.

SURVEY RESULTS	
Candidate A	15
Candidate B	34
Candidate C	32
Candidate D	19
Residents Surveyed: 100	

7. Candidate A ________ **8.** Candidate B ________ **9.** Candidate C ________ **10.** Candidate D ________

Predict the number of grocery shoppers who would pick a certain brand of orange juice.

Survey: A random sample of 100 grocery shoppers at a store that has 400 regular shoppers were asked what juice brand they like.

SURVEY RESULTS	
Sunny Kool	44
Orange Lite	21
Tropical Splash	35
People Surveyed: 100	

11. Sunny Kool ______ **12.** Orange Lite ______ **13.** Tropical Splash ______

Solve.

14. A survey found that mathematics is the favorite subject of 25% of the students surveyed. In a school of 216 students, how many would you expect to name mathematics as their favorite subject?

____

15. A woman has 2 children and is expecting a third. If her first 2 children are girls, what is the probability that her next child will be a boy?

____

Name: ______________________________

TREE DIAGRAMS AND THE COUNTING PRINCIPLE

For problems 1–3, draw a tree diagram to show all the possible outcomes. How many are there?

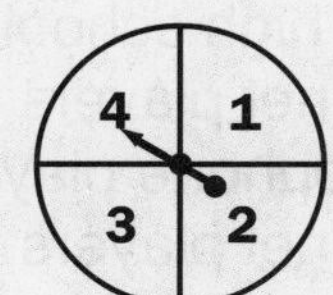

1. Spinning each spinner once

____

2. Tossing a coin once and rolling a number cube once

____

3. Selecting a pair of shoes and a pair of socks

____

Apparel	Color Choices
Shoes	Black, Brown, White
Socks	Black, White, Yellow, Red, Plaid

Find the total number of possible outcomes. Explain your methods.

4. Choosing a new pair of sneakers out of 5 styles in 4 colors

____

5. Ordering a sandwich at the deli by choosing 1 of 6 types of breads and 1 of 7 types of fillings

____

6. Picking out a pair of glasses from 8 styles in 3 colors

____

Solve.

7. Suppose you and four of your classmates each tossed a coin. What is the probability that everyone's toss would have an outcome of tails?

____

8. Each of 15 students is randomly assigned a seat in a classroom with 15 seats. What is the probability that any given student will sit in Row 1, Seat 1?

____

Name: ____________________

PROBLEM SOLVING: MAKE A TABLE

✔ Read
✔ Plan
✔ Solve
✔ Look Back

Solve using the make-a-table strategy.

1. In a high school band, there are 8 clarinet players for every 3 saxophone players. If there are 32 clarinet players, how many saxophone players are there?

   ____

2. In a book of band music, there are 3 John Philip Sousa pieces for every Duke Ellington piece. There are 2 Duke Ellington pieces for every 1 Count Basie piece. If there are 3 Count Basie pieces, how many Sousa pieces are there?

   ____

3. The school has 4 jazz bands, each with 9 members. In each jazz band there are 2 trombone players, 3 clarinet players, and 1 saxophone player. The rest are percussionists. How many of each type of player is there altogether?

   ____

   ____

   ____

4. The band teacher has a tape collection organized in alphabetical order. She has 3 tapes in the A–F section, 4 tapes in the G–K section, 1 tape in the L–R section, and 6 tapes in the S–Z section. If she had double the number of tapes in sections G–K and S–Z, how many tapes would she have altogether?

   ____

Solve using any method.

5. The numbers on a combination padlock range from 0 to 40. The combination to the padlock consists of 3 numbers. Suppose you can only remember the first 2 numbers of the combination. What is the greatest number of tries you would have to make to guess the correct combination?

   ____

6. When a number cube is rolled, there are 6 possible outcomes. When two cubes are rolled, there are 36 possible outcomes, and when three cubes are rolled, there are 216 possible outcomes. Based on that pattern, how many possible outcomes would there be if four number cubes were rolled?

   ____

Name: ______________________

PERIMETER AND AREA

Find the perimeter and the area for the rectangle.

1. 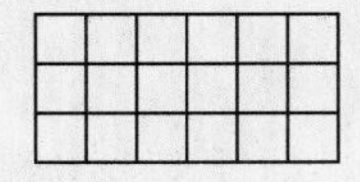

2. 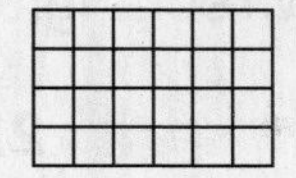

3. 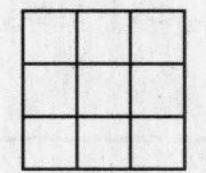

4. 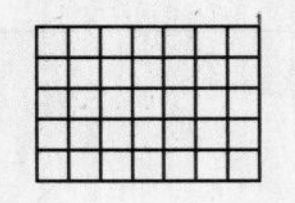

5. 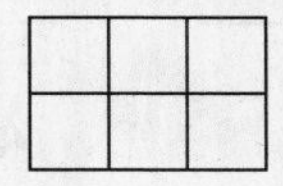

6.

7. 29 ft; 14 ft

8. 2.7 m; 6.25 m

9. $5\frac{1}{2}$ in.; $3\frac{3}{8}$ in.

For the given perimeter of a rectangle, find the possible length and width in whole numbers that will give the greatest area.

10. 14 ft

11. 18 mm

12. 22 m

13. 30 cm

14. 74 in.

15. 102 m

Solve.

16. A blueprint displays a rectangle where 5 in. by 7 in. is drawn to the scale 1 inch equals 4 ft. What is the perimeter of the actual rectangle?

17. Cathy's rectangular vegetable garden is $15\frac{1}{2}$ ft long and $3\frac{1}{2}$ ft wide. What is the area of her garden?

Name: ______________________________

ENLARGING RECTANGLES

Double and triple the length and width of the rectangle.
Find the perimeter and area of the new rectangle.

1. 8 ft by 1 ft

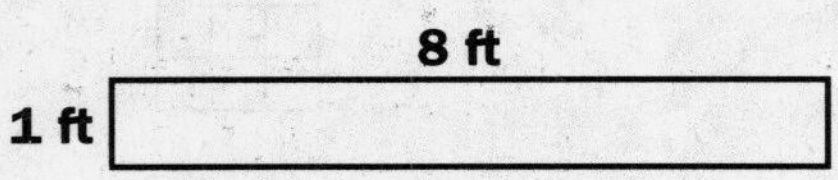

2. 3 m by 4 m

3. 12 mm by 5 mm

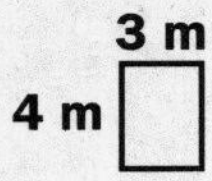

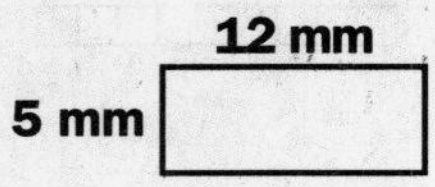

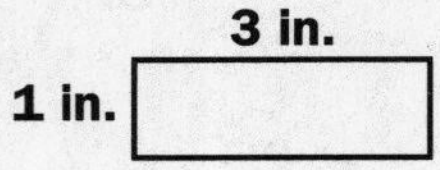

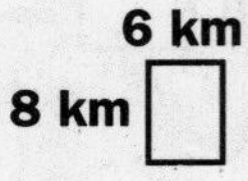

4. 3 in. by 1 in.

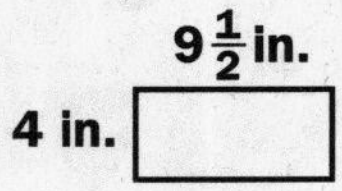

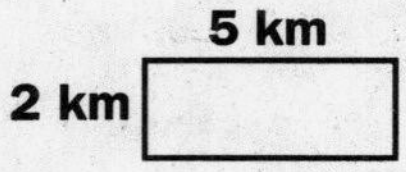

5. 6 km by 8 km

6. $9\frac{1}{2}$ in. by 4 in.

7. 5 km by 2 km

8. 4.5 m by 1.5 m

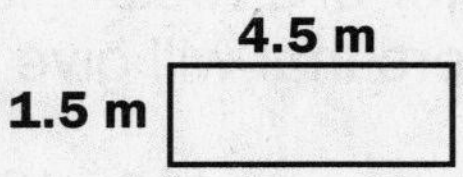

9. Length: 50 yd Width: 12 yd

10. Length: 90 ft Width: 40 ft

11. Length: 150 m Width: 100 m

12. Length: 1,250 ft Width: 550 ft

Name: ______________________

Practice 123

AREA OF PARALLELOGRAMS AND TRIANGLES

Find the area of the parallelogram.

1.
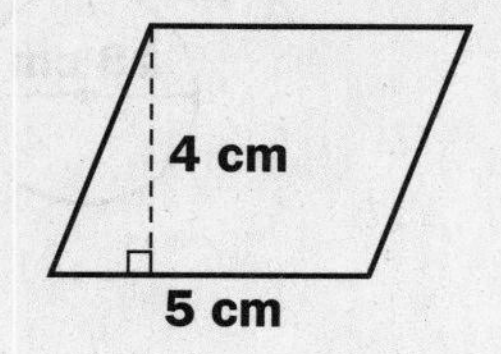

2.
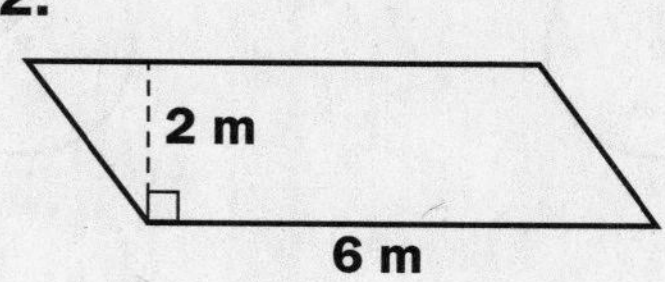

3.
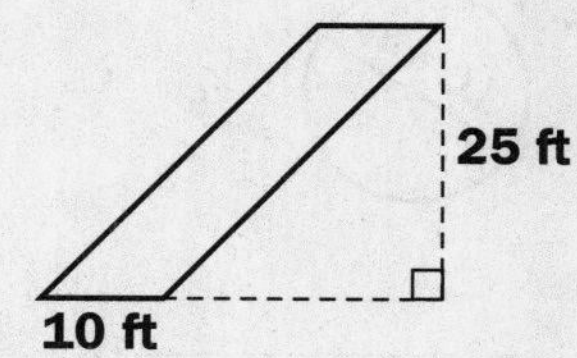

4.
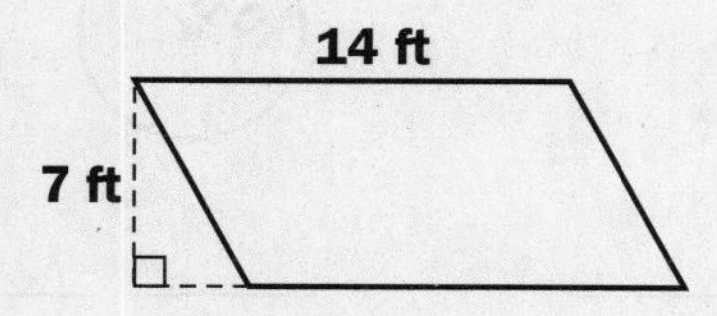

5.
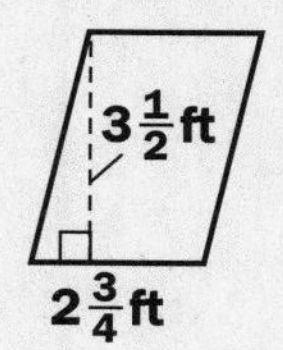

6.
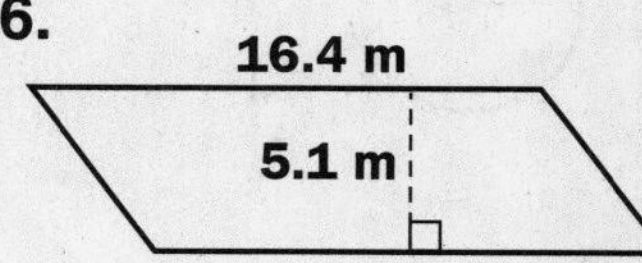

Find the area of the triangle.

7.
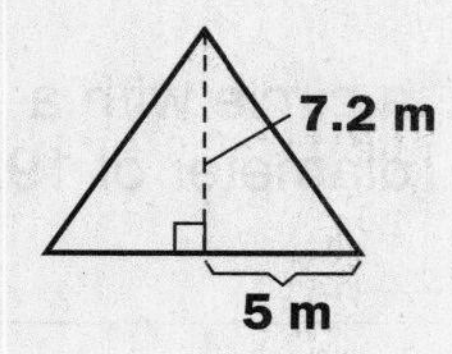

8.
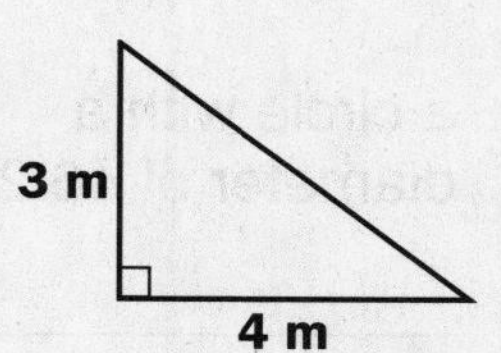

9.
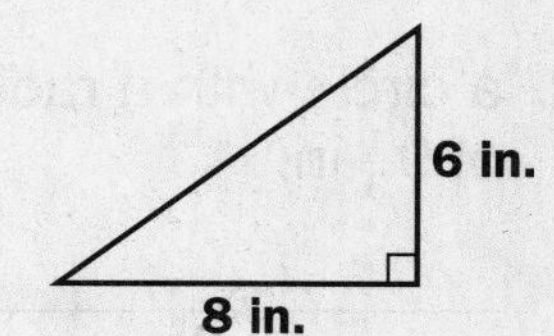

10.
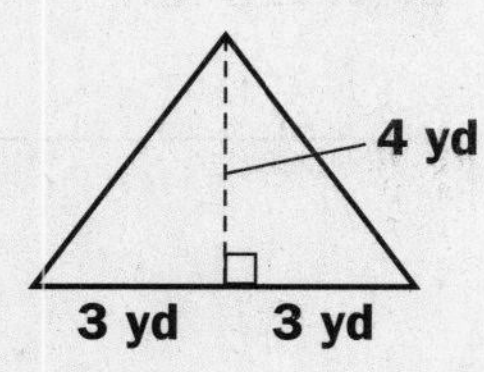

11.
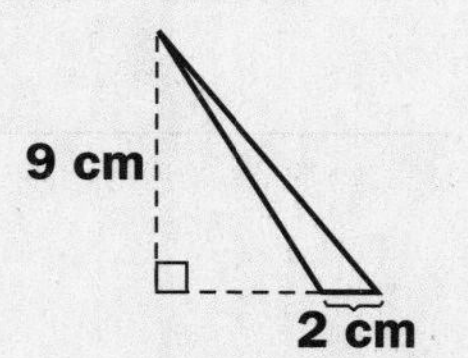

12.
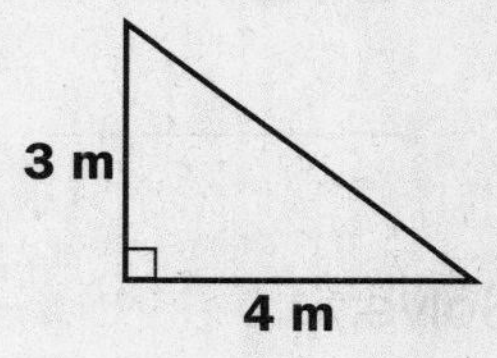

Solve.

13. An $8\frac{1}{2}$-by-11-inch rectangular piece of paper is cut in half along a diagonal. What is the height of each of the triangles formed by cutting the paper?

14. A triangle has a height of 16 centimeters and a base of 5 centimeters. What is the area of the triangle?

Name: ______________________

CIRCUMFERENCE OF A CIRCLE

Find the circumference of the circle. Use 3.14 or $3\frac{1}{7}$ for π and round to the nearest tenth for answers with decimals.

1. 

____

2. 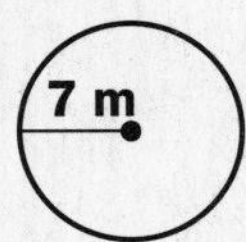

____

3. 

____

4. 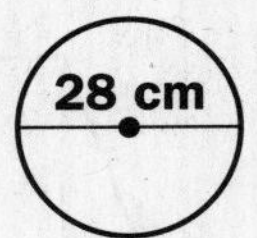

____

5. 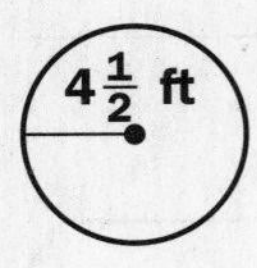

____

6. 

____

7. 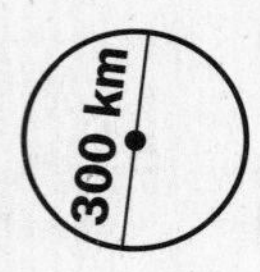

____

8. 

____

9. a circle with a diameter of 5.6 cm ______________

10. a circle with a radius of 12.8 m ______________

11. a circle with a diameter of $9\frac{1}{2}$ in. ______________

12. a circle with a radius of $9\frac{1}{3}$ in. ______________

13. a circle with a diameter of 46.23 cm ______________

14. a circle with a diameter of 19.3 m ______________

15. a circle with a radius of 6.34 km ______________

16. a circle with a diameter of 29 cm ______________

17. a circle with a radius of 17.26 km ______________

Solve.

18. The circumference of an automobile tire is about 70 inches. Ring the best estimate of the diameter of the tire.

    a. 10 in. b. 20 in.

    c. 30 in. d. 40 in.

19. Suppose you rolled these circles.

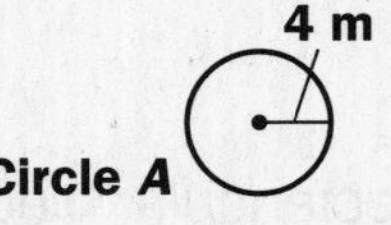

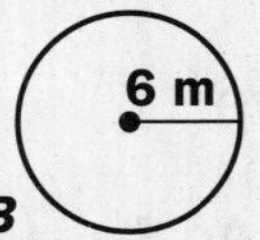

Which circle will roll farther in 3 complete revolutions? How much farther?

____

Name:

Practice 125

AREA OF A CIRCLE

Find the circumference and area of the circle. Use $\pi = 3.14$ or $3\frac{1}{7}$. Round to the nearest tenth for answers with decimals.

1. 

2. 

3. 

4. 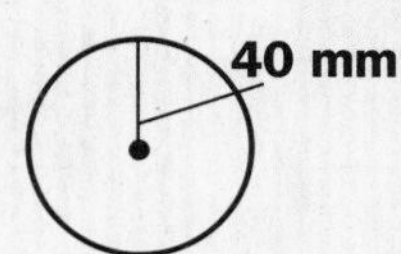

5. 

6. 

7. 

8. 

Algebra Fill in the chart. Use $\pi = 3.14$. Round to the nearest tenth.

	Radius	Diameter	Circumference	Area
9.	4 in.			
10.		27 km		
11.				9.6 sq cm
12.			47.1 ft	
13.		$4\frac{2}{5}$ mi		
14.				

Name: ______________________

Area of Compound Figures

Find the area of the shaded region. Use 3.14 for π. Round to the nearest tenth.

1. 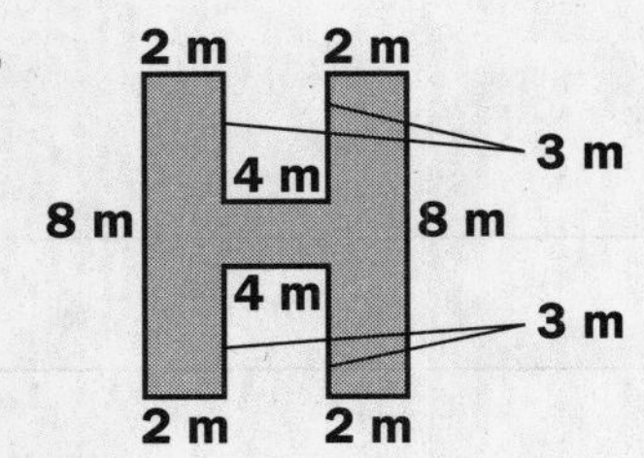

2. 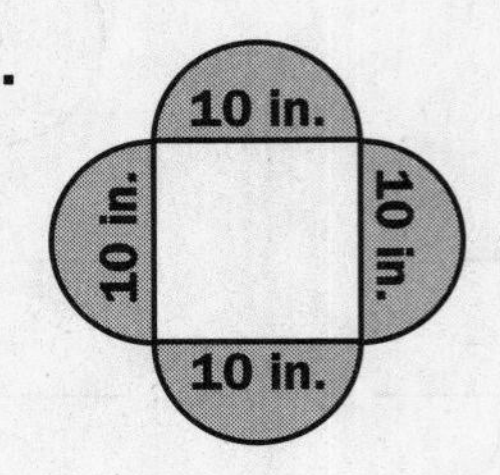

3. 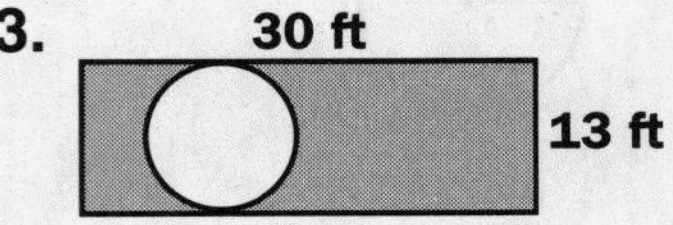

4. 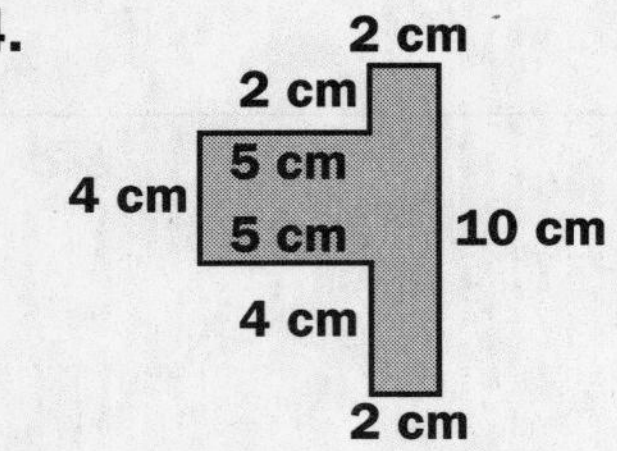

5. 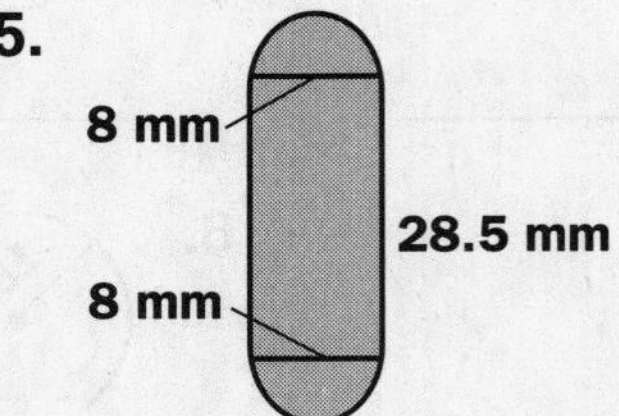

6. 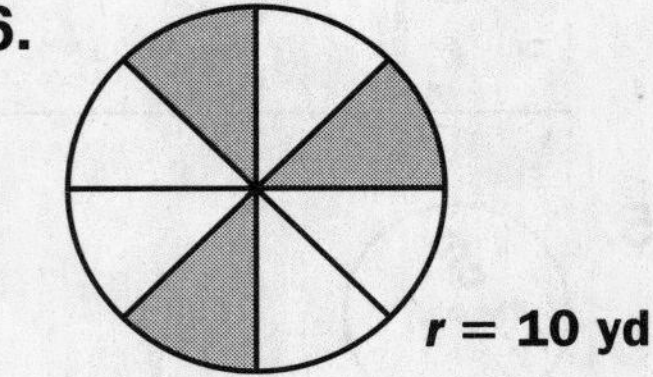

7. 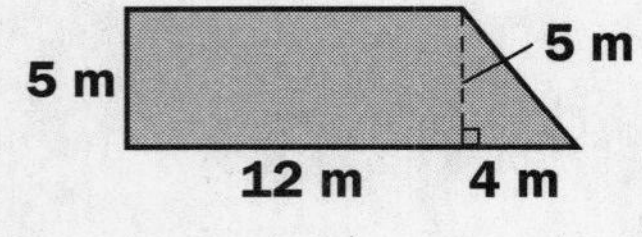

8. 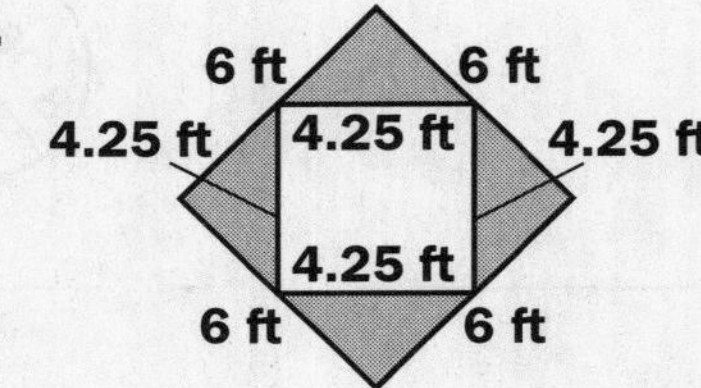

9. 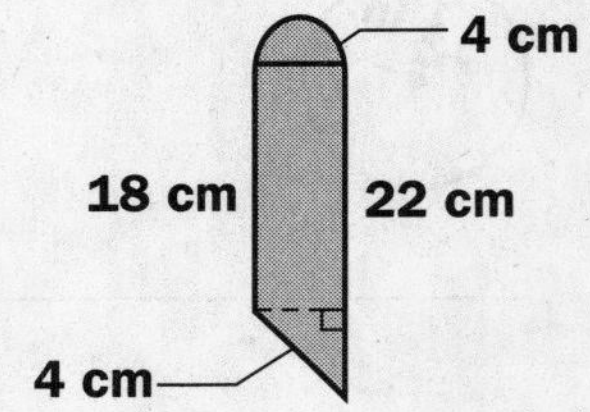

Solve. If necessary, round to the nearest tenth.

10. The only opening into a circular room is a 3-foot-wide door. The radius of the room is 15 feet. Suppose base molding is to be installed around the perimeter of the room. How many feet of molding should be purchased?

11. A 24-inch-by-18 inch picture frame is 3 inches wide on all sides. What area of the picture can be seen?

Name: ____________________

PROBLEM-SOLVING STRATEGY: MAKE A DIAGRAM

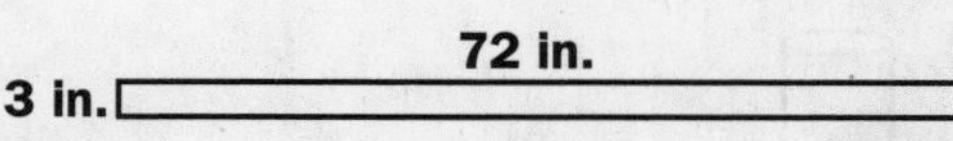

Solve using the make-a-diagram strategy.

1. The hardwood floor in the library of a castle needs to be replaced. The floor is rectangular and measures 32 feet by 48 feet. Each piece of new flooring that will be installed looks like the board at the right. What is the minimum number of boards that will be needed?

72 in.

3 in.

____

2. The floor of a castle dining room is shown at the right. Suppose the walls are 12 feet high with no windows, and there is one door measuring 8 feet by 10 feet. What is the total area of all of the walls of the dining room?

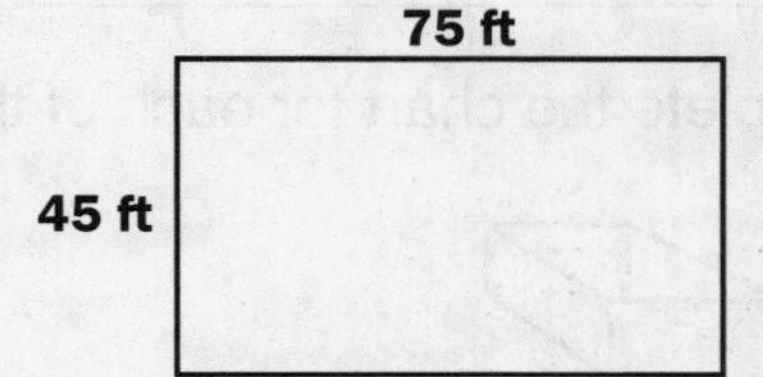

____

Solve using any method.

3. The bricks in a wall surrounding a castle include "soldiers." Soldiers, shown in the drawing at the right, are bricks turned vertically at the top of a wall. If there are an average of 2.5 soldiers per foot in the wall, and the perimeter of the wall is 2,150 feet, about how many soldiers can be found in the wall surrounding the castle?

____

____

4. A castle occupies 21,632 square feet of a 432,640-square-foot area of land. In simplest form, the area of the castle occupies what fraction of the area of the land?

____

5. The height of a castle wall is 18 feet and its length is 2,150 feet. The wall is made of brick. Each square foot of wall contains an average of 7.5 bricks. About how many bricks are in the wall?

____

Name: ______________________________

Classify 3-Dimensional Figures

Name the 3-dimensional figure.

1. ______________________________

2. ______________________________

3. ______________________________

4. ______________________________

Complete the chart for each of the following figures.

5.

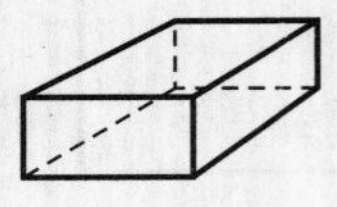

____

6.

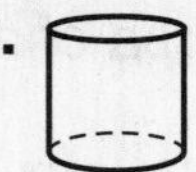

____

7.

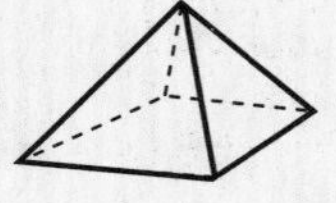

____

8.

____

Type of Solid Figure	Number of Bases and Faces	Number of Edges	Number of Vertices

Solve.

9. Find an example of a cylinder, a rectangular prism, a cube, and a sphere in your classroom.

____

____

10. Think about a penny and a nickel. What name would you use to describe their shape?

____

____

Name:

DIFFERENT VIEWS OF 3-DIMENSIONAL FIGURES

Sketch the top view, front view, and side view of the shape.

1. 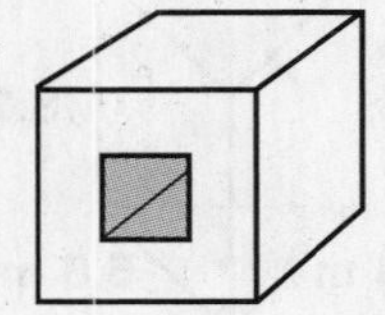

2. 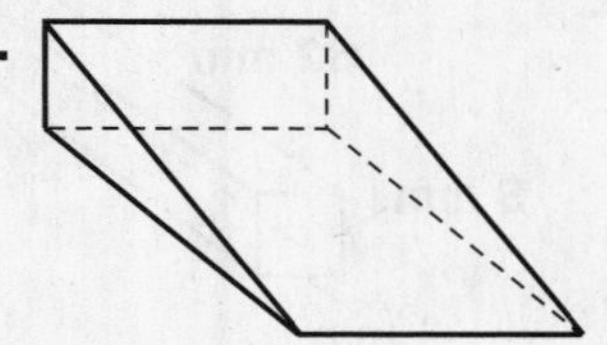

3. 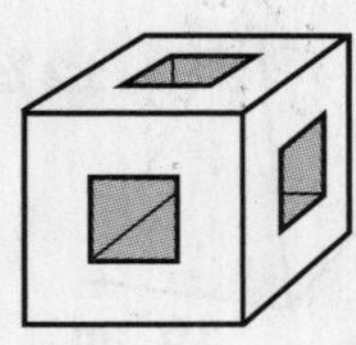

4. 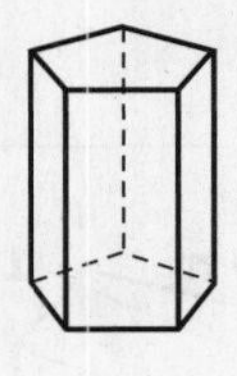

5. 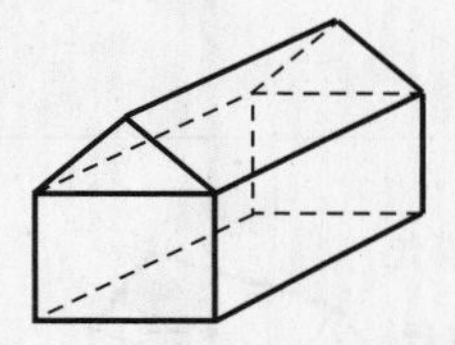

6. 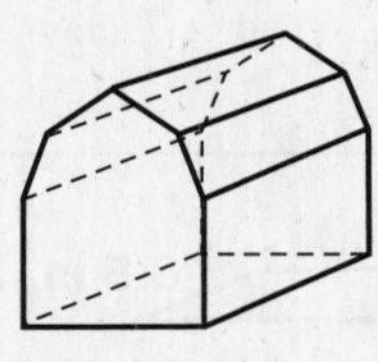

Decide what is the greatest and least number of cubes possible to build the figure.

7. 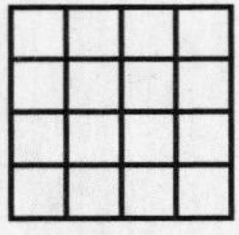
Top View

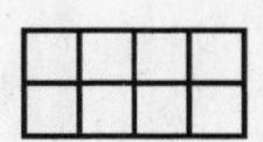
Front View

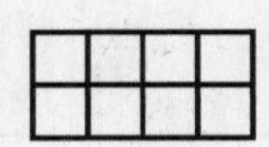
Side View

8. 
Top View

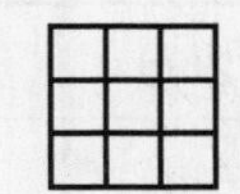
Front View

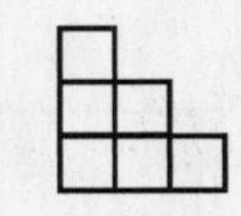
Side View

Solve.

9. A staircase formed from blocks is shown at the right. Sketch the top view, front view, and side view of the staircase.

Name: ______________________________

SURFACE AREA: PRISM

Find the surface area for each three-dimensional shape.
Round to the nearest tenth.

1.

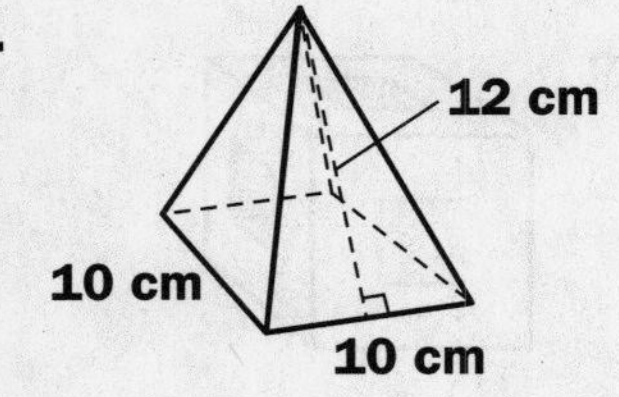

____

2.

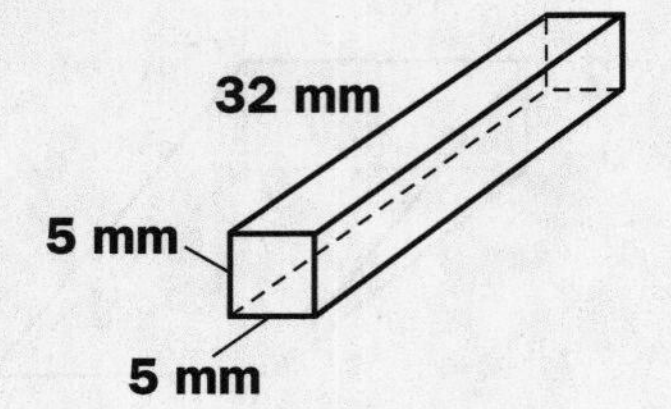

____

3.

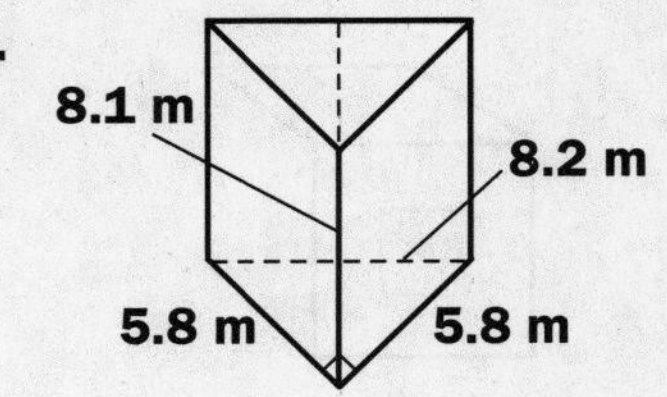

____

4.

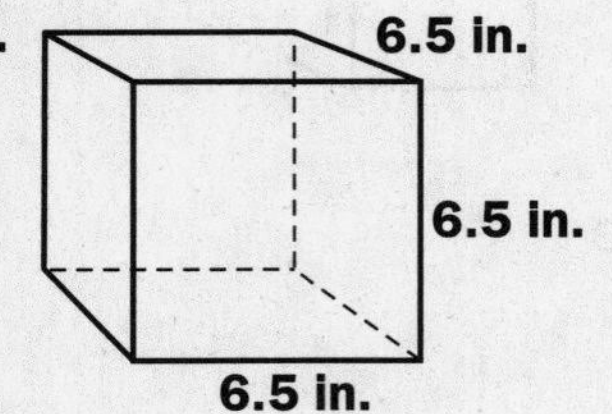

____

5.

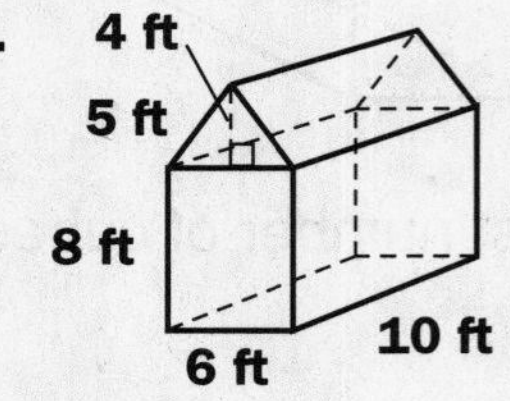

____

6.

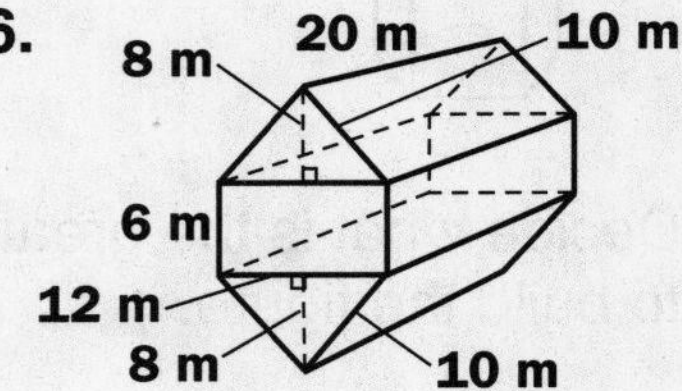

____

Algebra Complete the table for the rectangular prism.
Round to the nearest tenth.

	Length	Width	Height	Surface Area
7.	8 yd	4 yd	2 yd	
8.	12 ft		6 ft	360 ft²
9.		5.5 cm	5.5 cm	181.5 cm²

Name the 3-dimensional figure the net will make and find the surface area.

10.

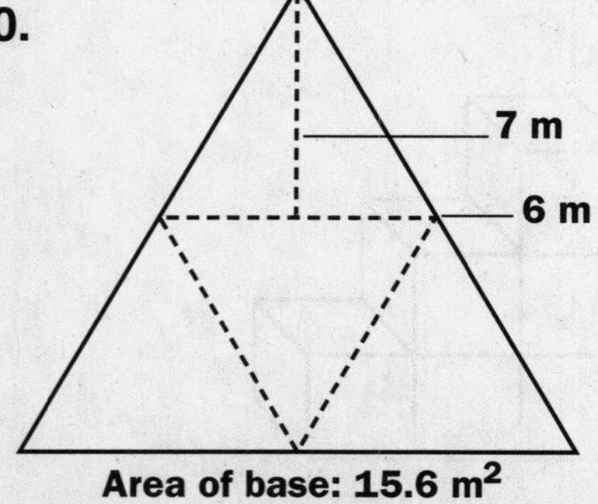

____

Name: ______________________

VOLUME

Find the volume for the rectangular prism. Round to the nearest tenth.

1.

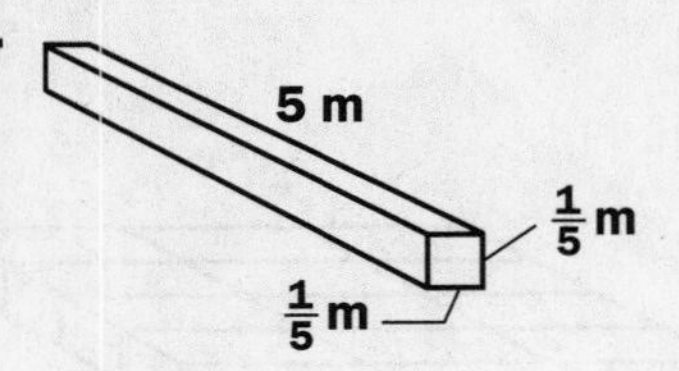

2.

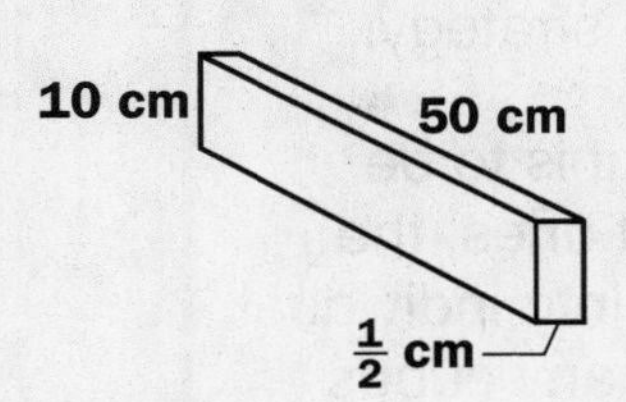

3.

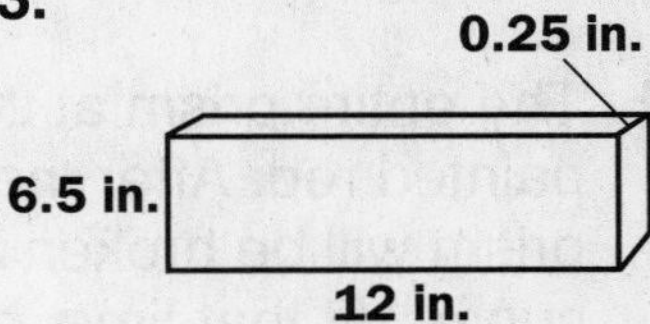

______ ______ ______

Find the total volume.

4.

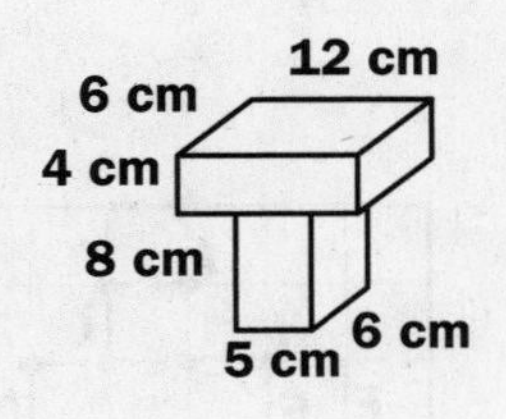

5.

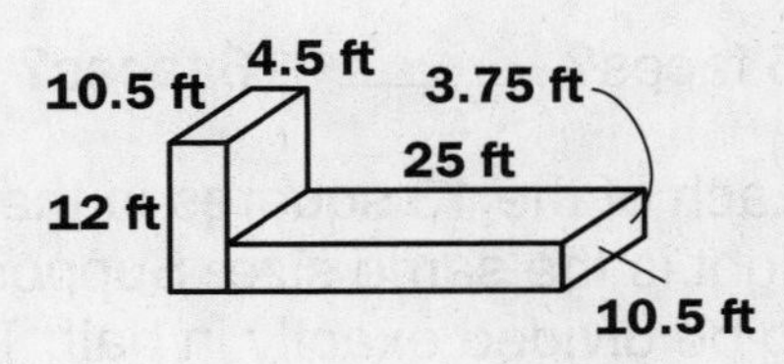

______ ______

6.

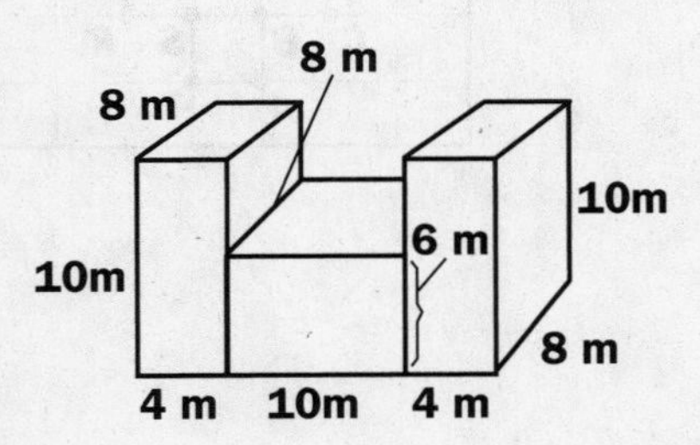

7.

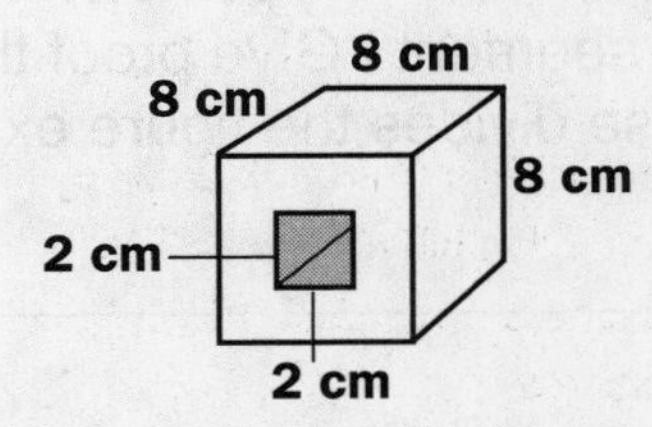

Hint: The hole goes all the way through the figure.

______ ______

Algebra. Complete the table for the rectangular prism. Round to the nearest tenth.

8.

Length	Width	Height	Surface Area
$5\frac{1}{2}$ ft	$4\frac{1}{4}$ ft	$7\frac{3}{8}$ ft	
2.9 m	3.5 m	4.8 m	
7 yd	$8\frac{1}{2}$ yd	$2\frac{3}{4}$ yd	

Name: ____________________

Problem Solving: Make a Model

✔ Read
✔ Plan
✔ Solve
✔ Look Back

Solve using the make-a-model strategy.

1. The entire prism at the right is to be painted red. After the paint dries, the prism will be broken apart into individual cubes. At that time, how many cubes will be painted red on

1 face? ______ 2 faces? ______

3 faces? ______ 4 faces? ______

5 faces? ______ 6 faces? ______

2. Each of the 13 squares in the figure at the right is the same size. Suppose the figure is to be divided exactly in half. The line segment used to divide the figure will begin at Point *A*. What point is the other end of the line segment? Give proof that the line you chose divides the figure exactly in half.

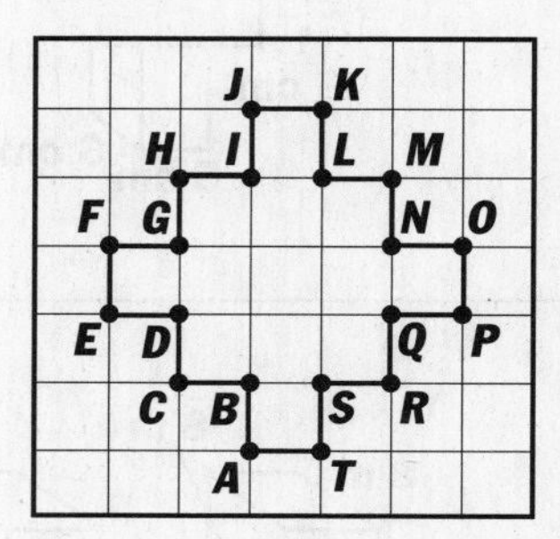

____

Solve using any method

3. Circles measuring 8 inches in diameter are being cut from a piece of cardboard measuring 30 inches by 65 inches. If 32 circles altogether are cut from the cardboard, about how many square inches are unused?

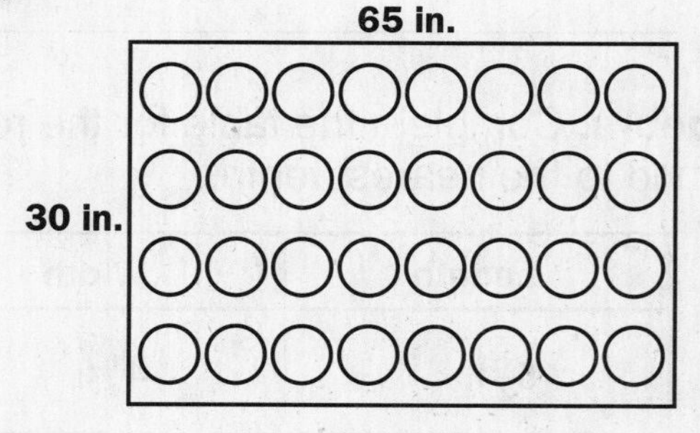

____

4. The triangles at the right are similar. Find the missing measures.

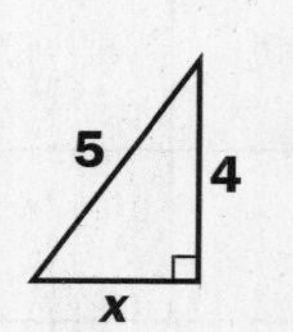

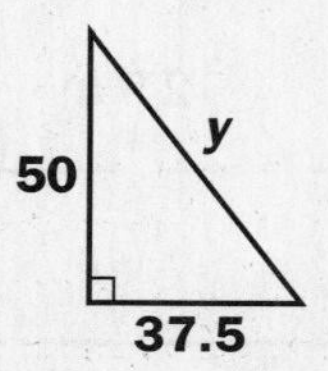

____

Name: ____________________

INTEGERS

Write an integer to represent each situation.

1. spend $3 ______
2. a gain of 4 yds in football ______
3. making a two-point basket ______
4. 8 degrees above zero ______
5. 11 degrees below zero ______
6. 1 ft below sea level ______
7. a deposit of $12 into a savings account ______
8. 10 seconds before the start of a race ______
9. height increase of 3 in. ______
10. running time decrease of 3 seconds ______
11. test score increase of 10 points ______
12. speed increase of 10 mph ______
13. 20 seconds before takeoff ______
14. allowance of $5 ______
15. reading 30 pages in a book ______
16. losing an hour of sleep ______

Write an integer to represent the situation. Then describe the opposite situation and write an integer to represent it.

17. stock market falls 20 points

____

____

18. 100 ft above sea level

____

____

19. earning $20

____

20. 12° above zero

____

21. 10 ft below ground

____

22. winning by 7 points

____

Describe a situation that can be represented by each integer.

23. +6 ____________________

24. ⁻25 ____________________

Name: ____________________

Compare and Order Integers

Compare. Write > or <. You may use a number line to help.

1. 5 ◯ 7	**2.** $^{-}1$ ◯ 3	**3.** 2 ◯ 0	**4.** $^{-}3$ ◯ $^{-}2$
5. 6 ◯ $^{-}6$	**6.** 0 ◯ $^{-}3$	**7.** 2 ◯ 6	**8.** 7 ◯ $^{-}5$
9. 0 ◯ $^{-}9$	**10.** 5 ◯ 8	**11.** $^{-}2$ ◯ $^{-}6$	**12.** 4 ◯ $^{-}1$
13. $^{-}7$ ◯ 2	**14.** 8 ◯ $^{-}4$	**15.** 0 ◯ $^{-}1$	**16.** $^{-}8$ ◯ $^{-}3$
17. 11 ◯ $^{-}11$	**18.** 23 ◯ 26	**19.** $^{-}18$ ◯ $^{-}20$	**20.** $^{-}26$ ◯ 5
21. $^{-}2$ ◯ $^{-}30$	**22.** $^{-}50$ ◯ $^{-}60$	**23.** 44 ◯ 23	**24.** 67 ◯ 87
25. 12 ◯ $^{-}23$	**26.** 34 ◯ 21	**27.** 67 ◯ 97	**28.** 12 ◯ 17

Write the integers in order from greatest to least.

29. $^{-}2$, 1, $^{-}1$ ____________________

30. 4, $^{-}4$, 3 ____________________

31. 0, $^{-}2$, $^{-}5$ ____________________

32. $^{-}3$, $^{-}6$, $^{-}4$ ____________________

33. 1, 0, 7 ____________________

34. $^{-}8$, $^{-}6$, 3 ____________________

35. 9, $^{-}8$, 8 ____________________

36. 2, $^{-}2$, $^{-}1$ ____________________

37. $^{-}1$, 5, 1, $^{-}5$ ____________________

38. $^{-}12$, $^{-}14$, 6, $^{-}9$ ____________________

39. 21, $^{-}24$, $^{-}20$, 22 ____________________

40. 33, $^{-}29$, $^{-}42$, 35 ____________________

41. 53, $^{-}51$, 54, 72 ____________________

42. $^{-}12$, 27, $^{-}32$, 54, $^{-}60$ ____________________

Solve.

43. The low temperature on Monday night was $^{-}8$°F. The low temperature was $^{-}6$°F on Tuesday night. Which night was colder?

____

44. The high temperature on Saturday was 0°C. The high temperature on Sunday was $^{-}2$°C. Which day was warmer?

____

Name: ____________________

ADD INTEGERS

Complete the number sentence represented by each model.

1. ⊖⊖⊖
⊕⊕⊕⊕

$^{-}3 + 4 =$ ____

2. ⊖⊖⊖⊖⊖⊖
⊕⊕⊕

$^{-}6 + 3 =$ ____

3. ⊖
⊖⊖⊖⊖

$^{-}1 + {}^{-}4 =$ ____

4. ⊕⊕⊕⊕
⊖⊖⊖⊖⊖

$4 + {}^{-}5 =$ ____

5. ⊖⊖
⊕⊕⊕⊕⊕⊕

$^{-}2 + 6 =$ ____

6. ⊖⊖⊖⊖⊖⊖⊖
⊖⊖⊖⊖

$^{-}7 + {}^{-}4 =$ ____

Add. You may use counters. Complete as many as you can mentally.

7. $^{-}1 + 7 =$ ____ **8.** $0 + {}^{-}2 =$ ____ **9.** $5 + 1 =$ ____

10. $^{-}4 + {}^{-}4 =$ ____ **11.** $6 + {}^{-}5 =$ ____ **12.** $^{-}7 + {}^{-}3 =$ ____

13. $^{-}8 + 6 =$ ____ **14.** $0 + {}^{-}1 =$ ____ **15.** $4 + {}^{-}7 =$ ____

16. $^{-}6 + {}^{-}5 =$ ____ **17.** $^{-}10 + {}^{-}5 =$ ____ **18.** $^{-}4 + 9 =$ ____

19. $^{-}10 + {}^{-}4 =$ ____ **20.** $1 + {}^{-}15 =$ ____ **21.** $^{-}12 + 9 =$ ____

22. $^{-}11 + 6 =$ ____ **23.** $12 + 4 =$ ____ **24.** $13 + {}^{-}6 =$ ____

25. $8 + {}^{-}9 =$ ____ **26.** $6 + {}^{-}6 =$ ____ **27.** $2 + {}^{-}7 =$ ____

28. $15 + {}^{-}11 =$ ____ **29.** $4 + {}^{-}3 =$ ____ **30.** $17 + {}^{-}9 =$ ____

31. $2 + {}^{-}3 + 1 =$ ____ **32.** $^{-}8 + 4 + {}^{-}1 =$ ____ **33.** $14 + {}^{-}2 + 3 =$ ____

34. $^{-}7 + 10 + {}^{-}3 =$ ____ **35.** $5 + {}^{-}6 + {}^{-}4 =$ ____ **36.** $12 + {}^{-}9 + 3 =$ ____

37. $10 + {}^{-}6 + 4 =$ ____ **38.** $13 + 5 + {}^{-}9 =$ ____ **39.** $3 + 5 + {}^{-}11 =$ ____

40. $14 + {}^{-}3 + {}^{-}9 =$ ____ **41.** $3 + 11 + {}^{-}14 =$ ____ **42.** $22 + 1 + {}^{-}2 =$ ____

Name: ____________________

SUBTRACT INTEGERS

Complete the number sentence represented by each model.

1. $^-3 - {}^-1 =$ _____

2. $4 - {}^-2 =$ _____

3. $^-6 - 4 =$ _____

4. $5 - {}^-4 =$ _____

5. $^-1 - {}^-4 =$ _____

6. $2 - {}^-9 =$ _____

Subtract. You may use a model.

7. $6 - {}^-3 =$ _____
8. $^-2 - {}^-7 =$ _____
9. $5 - 9 =$ _____
10. $^-8 - 2 =$ _____
11. $^-4 - {}^-8 =$ _____
12. $1 - 5 =$ _____
13. $^-1 - 6 =$ _____
14. $^-3 - {}^-3 =$ _____
15. $3 - 8 =$ _____
16. $^-5 - 1 =$ _____
17. $4 - 7 =$ _____
18. $^-6 - 4 =$ _____
19. $^-10 - {}^-2 =$ _____
20. $13 - {}^-6 =$ _____
21. $^-15 - 5 =$ _____
22. $^-12 - {}^-10 =$ _____
23. $18 - {}^-4 =$ _____
24. $11 - 14 =$ _____
25. $20 - 21 =$ _____
26. $^-23 - {}^-11 =$ _____

Complete.

27. $^-5 - {}^-3 = {}^-5 +$ _____ $=$ _____
28. $2 - 4 = 2 +$ _____ $=$ _____
29. $^-3 - 6 = {}^-3 +$ _____ $=$ _____
30. $^-1 - {}^-5 = {}^-1 +$ _____ $=$ _____
31. $^-6 - {}^-4 = {}^-6 +$ _____ $=$ _____
32. $9 - 10 = 9 +$ _____ $=$ _____
33. $8 - 13 = 8 +$ _____ $=$ _____
34. $^-11 - {}^-2 = {}^-11 +$ _____ $=$ _____
35. $14 - {}^-7 = 14 +$ _____ $=$ _____
36. $^-10 - {}^-10 = {}^-10 +$ _____ $=$ _____
37. $12 - 20 = 12 +$ _____ $=$ _____
38. $^-15 - {}^-8 = {}^-15 +$ _____ $=$ _____
39. $3 - {}^-7 = 3 +$ _____ $=$ _____
40. $^-5 - 12 = {}^-5 +$ _____ $=$ _____
41. $2 - 9 = 2 +$ _____ $=$ _____
42. $^-11 - 9 = {}^-11 +$ _____ $=$ _____
43. $2 - {}^-12 = 2 +$ _____ $=$ _____
44. $5 - 20 = 5 +$ _____ $=$ _____

Name: ______________________________

Practice 137

Problem-Solving Strategy: Use Logical Reasoning

✔ Read
✔ Plan
✔ Solve
✔ Look Back

Solve using the logical-reasoning strategy. Draw a Venn diagram to show your solution.

1. A meteorologist predicts the weather for the week. Three days will be sunny, 3 days will be cloudy, and 1 day will be sunny in the morning and cloudy in the afternoon. How many days will it be sunny? cloudy?

____

2. A meteorologist predicts that 5 days of one week will be cloudy. Two of those days it will also rain. How many days that week will be neither cloudy nor rainy?

____

3. On a rainy day, 342 students arrived at school. Of them, 113 students had umbrellas, 97 students wore hats, and 37 students did not have a hat or an umbrella. How many students had both an umbrella and a hat?

____

4. Maritza recorded the predictions of 4 meteorologists. One predicted a cloudy day, 1 predicted a sunny morning and a cloudy evening, 1 predicted a rainy day, and 1 predicted a sunny morning and a rainy evening. How many meteorologists predicted rain in any part of the day?

____

Solve using any method.

5. In a survey, 54 students said that Saturday was their favorite day of the week, and 31 students said that Sunday was their favorite day of the week. If 112 students were surveyed altogether, how many students chose a weekday as their favorite day of the week?

____

6. In a survey, 95 students said their favorite lunch was pizza. If this number of students represented $\frac{1}{4}$ of the total number surveyed, how many students were surveyed?

____

Name: ____________________

Coordinate Graphing in All Four Quadrants

Give the coordinates of each point.

1. B (______) **2.** H (______) **3.** C (______)

4. K (______) **5.** P (______) **6.** R (______)

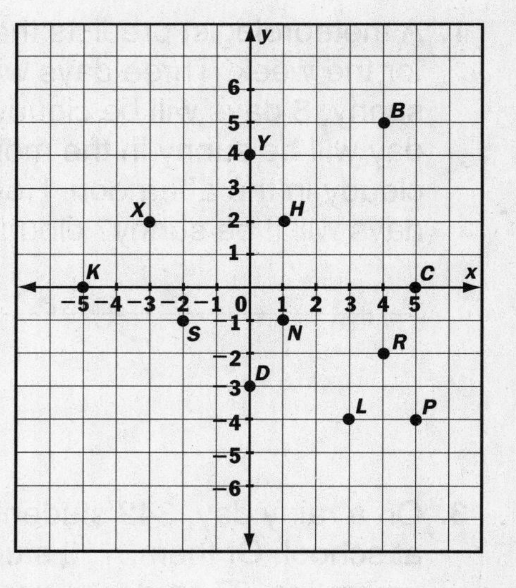

Name the point for each ordered pair.

7. $(1, {}^-1)$ ____ **8.** $({}^-3, 2)$ ____ **9.** $(0, {}^-3)$ ____

10. $(0, 4)$ ____ **11.** $(3, {}^-4)$ ____ **12.** $({}^-2, {}^-1)$ ____

Complete the table for the function represented by the equation. Then graph the function.

13. $y = x - 2$

x	y
$^-2$	
$^-1$	
0	
1	

14. $y = 5 - x$

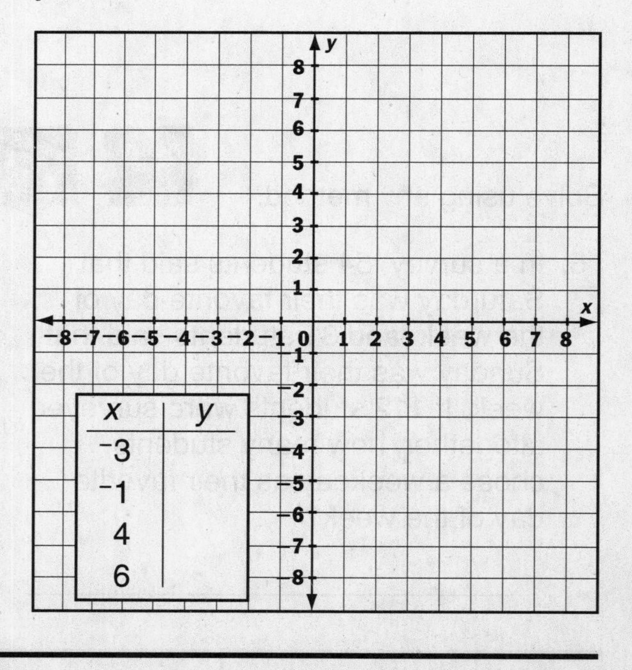

x	y
$^-3$	
$^-1$	
4	
6	

Name: ______________________________

Addition and Subtraction Equations

Write an addition and a subtraction equation for each model. Then solve both equations.

1. $x +$ ⊖⊖⊖ ⊖⊖ ⊕⊕

2. $t +$ ⊕ ⊖⊖⊖⊖

3. $r +$ ⊖⊖⊖ ⊖⊖⊖⊖ ⊖⊖ ⊖⊖

____

____

Solve each equation. You may use any method. Check the solution.

4. $x + 3 = {}^{-}1$ ____
5. $n - 4 = 6$ ____
6. $b - {}^{-}5 = {}^{-}2$ ____
7. $y + {}^{-}6 = 3$ ____
8. ${}^{-}2 = c + 4$ ____
9. $3 = m - {}^{-}7$ ____
10. ${}^{-}1 = r - 4$ ____
11. $5 = z + {}^{-}8$ ____
12. ${}^{-}1 - 4 = p$ ____
13. $6 - 8 = w$ ____
14. $2 - {}^{-}3 = d$ ____
15. ${}^{-}5 - {}^{-}9 = t$ ____
16. $n = {}^{-}8 + 7$ ____
17. $g = 9 - {}^{-}11$ ____
18. $q = {}^{-}12 + {}^{-}5$ ____
19. $s = {}^{-}10 - {}^{-}15$ ____
20. $a - {}^{-}6 = 13$ ____
21. $u + {}^{-}5 = 21$ ____
22. $v = 6 + {}^{-}12$ ____
23. $2 - 7 = k$ ____
24. $21 - g = {}^{-}6$ ____

Solve.

25. The outdoor temperature on one day in Minneapolis was ⁻12°F. At the same time, the outdoor temperature in Los Angeles was 71°F. Write an equation to find the range in temperatures between the two cities and solve it.

____

____

____

26. In the United States, the lowest temperature ever recorded was ⁻80°F in Alaska. The highest temperature ever recorded was 134°F in California. Write an equation to find the range in temperatures and solve it.

____

____

____

Name:

Problem Solving: Interpret Data

✔ Read
✔ Plan
✔ Solve
✔ Look Back

Solve. Use the table for problems 1–4.

RECORD TEMPERATURES FOR SEVEN STATES		
State	Low Temperature (in °F)	High Temperature (in °F)
Alabama	⁻27	112
California	⁻45	134
Connecticut	⁻32	105
Florida	⁻2	109
Idaho	⁻60	118
Massachusetts	⁻35	107
Minnesota	⁻59	125

1. Of the states listed, which has the lowest record temperature? the highest record temperature? ______

2. Which state has the greatest difference between its highest and lowest record temperature? What is the difference? ______

3. What is the difference between the record low temperatures of Minnesota and Florida? ______

4. For Alabama, what is the difference between the record low and record high temperature? ______

Solve using any method.

5. Mount McKinley in Alaska is 20,320 feet above sea level. Death Valley in California is 282 feet below sea level. What is the range of elevation between Mount McKinley and Death Valley? ______

6. The ratio of salt to water in a 20-ounce solution is 2 grams to 5 ounces. If a chemist adds 2 grams of salt to the solution, what is the ratio of salt to water in the new solution? ______

7. The ratio of male to female meteorologists in a state is 11:14. If the state has 175 meteorologists altogether, how many are male? How many are female? ______

8. In one hour, it rains 2.5 inches. It continues to rain at the same rate for the next three hours. How much rain will there be at the end of three hours? ______